A2 Maths Pocket Formula

Contents

Pure mathematics

Differentiation 1
Algebra and series 6
Integration 10
Curves 14
Differential equations 21
Vectors 24
Numerical methods 32

Mechanics

Projectiles 33
Kinematics and dynamics . . 36
Energy, work and power . . . 40
Momentum and collisions . . 43
Moments and equilibrium . . 47
Centre of mass 49
Circular motion 54
Further energy topics 60
Simple harmonic motion . . . 62

Statistics

The Poisson distribution 65
Continuous random variables 66
Approximating distributions 68
Samples and estimation 70
Hypothesis testing 74
Chi-squared distribution 83

Decision and discrete mathematics

Game theory 86
Recurrence relations 89
Coding 91
Index 93

Introduction

This Mathematics Pocket Formula Book was conceived after countless suggestions made by students for a comprehensive, easy-to-follow guide that covers all aspects of the syllabus.

It is suitable for any A-Level mathematics course based on the 2000 specifications. It is relevant to all examination boards and covers all modules.

This A2 book gives students step-by-step methods to solve many maths problems, with valuable commentary and advice. It contains 'All You Need To Know', so any student with full knowledge of this pocket book should be well prepared for the A2 exams.

Published by HarperCollins*Publishers* Limited
77–85 Fulham Palace Road
Hammersmith London W6 8JB
www.**fire**and**water**.com

> www.**Collins**Education.com
> Online support for schools and colleges

© HarperCollins*Publishers* Limited 2002
First published 2002
Reprinted 10 9 8 7 6 5 4 3 2 1
ISBN 0 00 713420 7

Jeff Geha asserts the moral right to be identified as the author of this work.

All rights reserved. No part of this publication may be reproduced, stored in a retrieval system, or transmitted in any form or by any means, electronic, mechanical, photocopying, recording or otherwise, without either the prior permission of the Publisher or a licence permitting restricted copying in the United Kingdom issued by the Copyright Licensing Agency Ltd., 90 Tottenham Court Road, London W1P 0LP.

This book is sold subject to the condition that it shall not by way of trade or otherwise be lent, hired out or otherwise circulated without the Publisher's prior consent.

British Library Cataloguing in Publication Data
A Catalogue record for this publication is available from the British Library.

Edited by Joan Miller
Designed by Merlin Group International and Ann Miller
Artwork by Merlin Group International and Caroline Miller
Cover design by Susi Martin-Taylor
Printed in Great Britain by Martins the Printers Ltd, Berwick upon Tweed

PURE MATHEMATICS — DIFFERENTIATION

The chain rule
AQA: P4; EDEXCEL: P3; OCR: P2; WJEC: P2; NICCEA: P2

$\dfrac{dy}{dx} = \dfrac{dy}{du} \times \dfrac{du}{dx}$, where y and u are functions of x.

Example
Differentiate $\dfrac{1}{5 - x^2}$.

Solution
Let $y = \dfrac{1}{5 - x^2}$, $u = 5 - x^2$.

$\therefore \; y = \dfrac{1}{u} = u^{-1}$

$\begin{aligned}
\dfrac{dy}{dx} &= \dfrac{dy}{du} \times \dfrac{du}{dx} \\
&= -u^{-2} \times -2x \\
&= 2x(5 - x^2)^{-2} \\
&= \dfrac{2x}{(5 - x^2)^2}
\end{aligned}$

The product rule
AQA: P4; EDEXCEL: P3; OCR: P3; WJEC: P2; NICCEA: P3

$\dfrac{d}{dx}(uv) = u\dfrac{dv}{dx} + v\dfrac{du}{dx}$

where u and v are functions of x.

The quotient rule
AQA: P4; EDEXCEL: P3; OCR: P3; WJEC: P2; NICCEA: P3

$\dfrac{d}{dx}\left(\dfrac{u}{v}\right) = \dfrac{v\dfrac{du}{dx} - u\dfrac{dv}{dx}}{v^2}$

where u and v are functions of x.

Note: With the quotient rule v must be the denominator and u the numerator.

PURE MATHEMATICS — DIFFERENTIATION

Logarithmic functions
AQA: P4; EDEXCEL: P2; OCR: P2; WJEC: P2; NICCEA: P2

$$\frac{d}{dx}\ln(f(x)) = \frac{f'(x)}{f(x)}$$

Trigonometric functions
AQA: P4; EDEXCEL: P3; OCR: P3; WJEC: P2; NICCEA: P3

You need to know the derivatives of the three main trigonometric functions.

$$\frac{d}{dx}(\sin f(x)) = f'(x)\cos f(x)$$

$$\frac{d}{dx}(\sin^n x) = n\sin^{n-1}x \times \frac{d}{dx}(\sin x) = n\cos x \sin^{n-1}x$$

$$\frac{d}{dx}(\cos f(x)) = -f'(x)\sin f(x)$$

$$\frac{d}{dx}(\cos^n x) = n\cos^{n-1}x \times \frac{d}{dx}(\cos x) = -n\sin x \cos^{n-1}x$$

$$\frac{d}{dx}(\tan f(x)) = f'(x)\sec^2 f(x)$$

$$\frac{d}{dx}(\tan^n x) = n\tan^{n-1}x \times \frac{d}{dx}(\tan x) = n\sec^2 x \tan^{n-1}x$$

For A2 level, you are expected to differentiate more complex functions, using any number of the above differentiation rules.

Example

Differentiate the following with respect to x.

a $\ln(\sin 3x)$ **b** $e^{2x}\cos x$ **c** $\dfrac{\ln x}{x}$

d $e^{\tan x^2}$ **e** $2\sin^2(3x + 2)$

Solution

a $\dfrac{d}{dx}\left(\ln(\sin 3x)\right) = \dfrac{\frac{d}{dx}(\sin 3x)}{\sin 3x} = \dfrac{3\cos 3x}{\sin 3x} = 3\cot 3x$

b Let $u = e^{2x}$ and $v = \cos x$.

$\dfrac{d}{dx}(uv) = u\dfrac{dv}{dx} + v\dfrac{du}{dx}$ *Product rule*

Pure Mathematics — Differentiation

$$= e^{2x} \times -\sin x + \cos x \times 2e^{2x}$$
$$= e^{2x}(2\cos x - \sin x)$$

Note: From the AS course $\frac{d}{dx}(e^{f(x)}) = f'(x)\,e^{f(x)}$

c Let $u = \ln x$ and $v = x$.

$$\frac{d}{dx}\left(\frac{u}{v}\right) = \frac{v\dfrac{du}{dx} - u\dfrac{dv}{dx}}{v^2}$$

$$= \frac{x \times \dfrac{1}{x} - \ln x \times 1}{x^2}$$

$$= \frac{1 - \ln x}{x^2}$$

d Let $y = e^{\tan x^2}$ and $u = \tan x^2$ i.e. $y = e^u$.

$$\frac{dy}{dx} = \frac{dy}{du} \times \frac{du}{dx} \qquad \text{Chain rule}$$
$$= e^u \times 2x \sec^2 x^2$$
$$= 2x\, e^{\tan x^2} \sec^2 x^2$$

e Let $y = 2\sin^2(3x + 2)$ and $u = \sin(3x + 2)$ i.e. $y = 2u^2$.

$$\frac{dy}{dx} = \frac{dy}{du} \times \frac{du}{dx} \qquad \text{Chain rule}$$
$$= 4u \times 3\cos(3x + 2)$$
$$= 12\sin(3x + 2)\cos(3x + 2)$$

Differentiation of inverse functions
AQA: P4; EDEXCEL: P3; OCR: P3; WJEC: P5; NICCEA: P3

$$\frac{dy}{dx} = \frac{1}{\left(\dfrac{dx}{dy}\right)}$$

Note: This rule only applies for first-order differentiation.

Example

If $x = \ln(y^2 - 2y + 1)$, find $\frac{dy}{dx}$.

Solution

$x = \ln(y^2 - 2y + 1)$

$\frac{dx}{dy} = \frac{2y - 2}{y^2 - 2y + 1}$

$\frac{dy}{dx} = \frac{y^2 - 2y + 1}{2y - 2} = \frac{(y-1)^2}{2(y-1)} = \frac{y-1}{2}$

Approximate changes
AQA: P4

For a small change (or error) δx in the value of x, the corresponding small change (or error) δy in the value of y is approximated by:

$\delta y \approx \frac{\delta y}{\delta x} \delta x$

Example

Find the approximate change in the volume of a sphere if the radius is increased from 4 cm to 4.01 cm.

Solution

$V_{\text{sphere}} = \frac{4}{3}\pi r^3$

$\therefore \frac{dV}{dr} = 3 \times \frac{4}{3}\pi r^2 = 4\pi r^2$

Now, $dV \approx \frac{dV}{dr} + \delta r \approx 4\pi r^2 \delta r$ **(1)**

Substituting $r = 4$, $\delta r = 0.01$ in (1) above:

$\delta V \approx 4\pi \times 4^2 \times 0.01 = 2.01$

The increase in the volume of the sphere is approximately 2 cm^3.

PURE MATHEMATICS   **DIFFERENTIATION**

Points of inflexion
AQA: P5

A **point of inflexion** on the curve $y = f(x)$ occurs if, at that point:

$\frac{d^2y}{dx^2} = 0$ and $\frac{d^3y}{dx^3} \neq 0$

Note: If $\frac{dy}{dx} = 0$ at that point as well, then the point of inflexion is a

horizontal point of inflexion.

Small angle approximations
OCR: M3; NICCEA: P4

If x is measured in radians and $|x|$ is small, the following small angle approximations for the three main trigonometric functions are valid.

$\sin x \approx x \quad \tan x \approx x \quad \cos x \approx 1 - \frac{1}{2}x^2$

Example

Find small angle approximations to the following, where x is measured in radians.

a $\dfrac{x + \sin 2x}{x^2}$ **b** $\dfrac{1 + \cos 2x}{1 - \tan x}$

Solution

a $\dfrac{x + \sin 2x}{x^2} \approx \dfrac{x + 2x}{x^2} = \dfrac{3x}{x^2} = \dfrac{3}{x}$

b $\dfrac{1 + \cos 2x}{1 - \tan x} \approx \dfrac{1 + \left(1 - \dfrac{(2x)^2}{2}\right)}{1 - x} = \dfrac{2 - 2x^2}{1 - x} = \dfrac{2(1-x)(1+x)}{(1-x)} = 2(1 + x)$

Pure Mathematics — Algebra and Series

Binomial series for rational numbers

AQA: P5; EDEXCEL: P3; OCR: P3; WJEC: P3; NICCEA: P3

When n is rational, $(1 + x)^n$ can be written as a series, using the **binomial expansion**.

$$(1 + x)^n = 1 + nx + \frac{n(n-1)}{2!}x^2 + \frac{n(n-1)(n-2)}{3!}x^3 + \ldots$$

For any rational n, the series converges provided $|x| < 1$.

Similarly, the binomial expansion $(1 + ax)^n$, for any rational n, converges provided $|x| < \frac{1}{a}$.

Note: Always state the values of x for which the series converges (or is valid), even if you are not specifically asked to do so.

Example

Find a cubic function that approximates to $\dfrac{1}{\sqrt{1+2x}}$ for small values of x. Hence, find $(130)^{-\frac{1}{2}}$ correct to 3 decimal places.

Solution

$$\frac{1}{\sqrt{1+2x}} = (1+2x)^{-\frac{1}{2}}$$

$$= 1 + \left(-\frac{1}{2}\right)(2x) + \frac{\left(-\frac{1}{2}\right)\left(-\frac{3}{2}\right)}{2!}(2x)^2 + \frac{\left(-\frac{1}{2}\right)\left(-\frac{3}{2}\right)\left(-\frac{5}{2}\right)}{3!}(2x)^3 + \ldots$$

$$= 1 - x + \frac{3}{2}x^2 - \frac{5}{2}x^3 + \ldots$$

The series converges provided $|x| < \frac{1}{2}$ i.e. $-\frac{1}{2} < x < \frac{1}{2}$.

Now $(130)^{-\frac{1}{2}} = (100 \times 1.3)^{-\frac{1}{2}} = \dfrac{(1.3)^{-\frac{1}{2}}}{\sqrt{100}} = \dfrac{(1.3)^{-\frac{1}{2}}}{10}$

To approximate $(1.3)^{-\frac{1}{2}}$, let $x = 0.15$.

Then $(1.3)^{-\frac{1}{2}} \approx 1 - (0.15) + \frac{3}{2}(0.15)^2 - \frac{5}{2}(0.15)^3 + \ldots$
$= 0.875$ (3 d.p.)

$\therefore (130)^{-\frac{1}{2}} \approx 0.088$ (3 d.p.)

Graphs of rational functions

AQA: P5; EDEXCEL: P3; OCR: P4; NICCEA: P3

A rational function is of the form $\frac{f(x)}{g(x)}$, where f(x) and g(x) are polynomials in x.

When you are graphing rational functions, it is important to identify asymptotes. There are three types.

- **Vertical asymptotes**

  In terms of $y = \frac{f(x)}{g(x)}$, vertical asymptotes exist when $g(x) = 0$.
  f(x) is irrelevant.

- **Horizontal and slant asymptotes**

  These are found by determining $\lim_{x \to \infty} \frac{f(x)}{g(x)}$, if it exists.

Once you have identified the asymptotes, use calculus to sketch graphs of the functions, indicating stationary points and points of inflexion. Indicate axial intercepts where appropriate.

Example

Identify all the asymptotes of $f(x) = \frac{2x^2 - 1}{(x + 2)(x - 3)}$.

Solution

f(x) is undefined for $x = -2$ and $x = 3$.

$\therefore x = -2$ and $x = 3$ are vertical asymptotes.

$\lim_{x \to \infty} f(x) = 2$ so $y = 2$ is a horizontal asymptote.

PURE MATHEMATICS   ALGEBRA AND SERIES

The remainder theorem
AQA: P4; EDEXCEL: P3; OCR: P2; WJEC: P2; NICCEA: P2

If a polynomial P(x) is divided by $(x - a)$ the remainder is given by P(a).

Partial fractions
AQA: P4; EDEXCEL: P3; OCR: P2; WJEC: P2; NICCEA: P2

Rational functions can sometimes be decomposed into **partial fractions**. There are four possibilities.

- **Linear factors in the denominator**

Example
Express $\dfrac{4x - 2}{(x + 1)(x - 1)}$ in partial fractions.

Solution
$$\frac{4x - 2}{(x + 1)(x - 1)} \equiv \frac{A}{(x + 1)} + \frac{B}{(x - 1)} = \frac{A(x - 1) + B(x + 1)}{(x + 1)(x - 1)}$$

$\Rightarrow 4x - 2 \equiv A(x - 1) + B(x + 1)$

When $x = 1$: $2 = 2B$ $\Rightarrow B = 1$
When $x = -1$: $^-6 = {^-}2A$ $\Rightarrow A = 3$

$\therefore \dfrac{4x - 2}{(x + 1)(x - 1)} \equiv \dfrac{3}{(x + 1)} + \dfrac{1}{(x - 1)}$

- **Non-factorising quadratic factors in the denominator**

Example
Express $\dfrac{10}{(x - 2)(x^2 + 1)}$ in partial fractions.

Solution
$$\frac{10}{(x - 2)(x^2 + 1)} \equiv \frac{A}{(x - 2)} + \frac{Bx + C}{(x^2 + 1)} \Rightarrow 10 \equiv A(x^2 + 1) + (Bx + C)(x - 2)$$

When $x = 2$: $10 = 5A$ $\Rightarrow A = 2$
When $x = 0$: $10 = A - 2C$ $\Rightarrow C = {^-}4$
When $x = 1$: $10 = 2A - B - C$ $\Rightarrow B = {^-}2$

$\therefore \dfrac{10}{(x - 2)(x^2 + 1)} \equiv \dfrac{2}{(x - 2)} - \dfrac{(2x + 4)}{(x^2 + 1)}$

Pure Mathematics — Algebra and Series

• Repeated factors in the denominator

Example

Express $\dfrac{14 + 2x}{(x + 1)^2(x + 2)}$ in partial fractions.

Solution

$$\frac{14 + 2x}{(x + 1)^2(x + 2)} \equiv \frac{A}{x + 2} + \frac{B}{x + 1} + \frac{C}{(x + 1)^2}$$

$$\Rightarrow 14 + 2x \equiv A(x + 1)^2 + B(x + 1)(x + 2) + C(x + 2)$$

When $x = -2$: $10 = A$ $\Rightarrow A = 10$
When $x = -1$: $12 = C$ $\Rightarrow C = 12$
When $x = 0$: $14 = A + 2B + 2C$ $\Rightarrow B = -10$

$$\therefore \frac{14 + 2x}{(x + 1)^2(x + 2)} \equiv \frac{10}{x + 2} - \frac{10}{x + 1} + \frac{12}{(x + 1)^2}$$

• Improper fractions

Improper fractions are fractions in which the highest power in the numerator is greater than or equal to the highest power in the denominator.

Improper fractions can be rewritten in a form which includes only proper fractions, by dividing the denominator into the numerator.

Example

Express $\dfrac{x^2}{x - 1}$ as a sum of partial fractions.

Solution

$$\frac{x^2}{x - 1} \equiv Ax + B + \frac{C}{x - 1} \Rightarrow x^2 \equiv (Ax + B)(x - 1) + C$$

When $x = 1$: $1 = C$ $\Rightarrow C = 1$
When $x = 0$: $0 = -B + C$ $\Rightarrow B = 1$
When $x = 2$: $4 = 2A + B + C$ $\Rightarrow A = 1$

$$\therefore \frac{x^2}{x - 1} \equiv x + 1 + \frac{1}{x - 1}$$

PURE MATHEMATICS   **INTEGRATION**

Trigonometric functions

AQA: P4; EDEXCEL: P3; OCR: P3; WJEC: P2; NICCEA: P3

You need to know the integrals of the three main trigonometric functions.

$$\int \sin(ax)\,dx = -\frac{1}{a}\cos(ax) + C$$

$$\int \cos(ax)\,dx = \frac{1}{a}\sin(ax) + C$$

$$\int \sec^2(ax)\,dx = \frac{1}{a}\tan(ax) + C$$

You should also be able to perform a one-step process based on observation.

$$\int \sin^n x \cos x\,dx = \frac{1}{n+1}\sin^{n+1} x + C$$

$$\int \cos^n x \sin x\,dx = \frac{-1}{n+1}\cos^{n+1} x + C$$

You will be expected to find the answer by thinking of the function that, when differentiated, simplifies to the given integral. For example:

$$\int 3\sin^2 x \cos x\,dx = \sin^3 x + C$$
$$\int \cos^3 x \sin x\,dx = -\frac{1}{4}\cos^4 x + C$$

Even powers of $\sin x$ and $\cos x$

These functions are integrated by using the double-angle identities covered in the AS course.

$$\sin^2 x = \frac{1}{2}(1 - \cos 2x)$$

$$\cos^2 x = \frac{1}{2}(1 + \cos 2x)$$

Generalising these results leads to:

$$\sin^2 ax = \frac{1}{2}(1 - \cos 2ax)$$

$$\cos^2 ax = \frac{1}{2}(1 + \cos 2ax)$$

PURE MATHEMATICS — INTEGRATION

You can apply the above substitutions to find the integrals of $\sin^2 x$ and $\cos^2 x$.

$\int \sin^2 x \, dx = \frac{1}{2}\int (1 - \cos 2x)\, dx = \frac{1}{2}(x - \frac{1}{2}\sin 2x) + C$

$\int \cos^2 x \, dx = \frac{1}{2}\int (1 + \cos 2x)\, dx = \frac{1}{2}(x + \frac{1}{2}\sin 2x) + C$

Use the double-angle results to integrate higher even powers of $\sin x$ and $\cos x$.

$\int \sin^4 x \, dx = \int [\frac{1}{2}(1 - \cos 2x)]^2 \, dx$

$= \frac{1}{4} \int (1 - 2\cos 2x + \cos^2 2x)\, dx$

$= \frac{1}{4}(x - \sin 2x) + \frac{1}{4}\int \cos^2 2x \, dx$

$= \frac{1}{4}(x - \sin 2x) + \frac{1}{4}\int \frac{1}{2}(1 + \cos 4x)\, dx$

$= \frac{1}{4}(x - \sin 2x) + \frac{1}{8}(x + \frac{1}{4}\sin 4x) + C$

Odd powers of $\sin x$ and $\cos x$

To integrate these functions, rewrite the function and use the one-step process described earlier.

$\int \cos^3 x \, dx = \int \cos x (\cos^2 x) \, dx$

$= \int \cos x (1 - \sin^2 x) \, dx$

$= \int (\cos x - \cos x \sin^2 x)\, dx$

$= \sin x - \frac{1}{3}\sin^3 x + C$

Integrals leading to a logarithmic function
AQA: P4; EDEXCEL: P2; OCR: P3; WJEC: P3; NICCEA: P3

Integrate functions of the form $\frac{f'(x)}{f(x)}$, using the logarithmic function.

$\int \frac{f'(x)}{f(x)} \, dx = \ln |f(x)| + C$

PURE MATHEMATICS — INTEGRATION

Example
Find: **a** $\int \frac{9x}{3+x^2} dx$ **b** $\int \frac{2e^x}{5+e^x} dx$

Solution
a $\int \frac{9x}{3+x^2} dx = \frac{9}{2}\int \frac{2x}{3+x^2} dx = \frac{9}{2}\ln|3+x^2| + C$

b $\int \frac{2e^x}{5+e^x} dx = 2\int \frac{e^x}{5+e^x} dx = 2\ln(5+e^x) + C$

Note: Change the numerator to the derivative of the denominator. The constant before the integral converts it to its original form.

Partial fractions
AQA: P4; EDEXCEL: P3; OCR: P3; WJEC: P3; NICCEA: P3

To integrate a rational function, try expressing it as partial fractions.

Example
Find: $\int \frac{2}{(x-1)(x-3)} dx$.

Solution
$\int \frac{2}{(x-1)(x-3)} dx = \int \left(\frac{1}{x-3} - \frac{1}{x-1} \right) dx = \ln|x-3| - \ln|x-1| + C$

$= \ln\left|\frac{X-3}{X-1}\right| + C$

Integration by substitution
AQA: P5; EDEXCEL: P3; OCR: P3; WJEC: P3; NICCEA: P3

You can find more difficult integrals by using a substitution to transform the integral from one expressed in, say, x to an easier one expressed in terms of a related variable, say, u.

Step 1: Choose a suitable substitution to replace x, i.e. $u = f(x)$, and find $\frac{du}{dx}$.

Step 2: Replace dx by $\frac{dx}{du} du$.

Step 3: Integrate the new function of u, then substitute $u = f(x)$.

Pure mathematics — Integration

Example
Find: $\int \dfrac{2x^3}{\sqrt{1+x^4}}\,dx$.

Solution
Step 1: Let $u = 1 + x^4 \Rightarrow \dfrac{du}{dx} = 4x^3$

Step 2: $dx = \dfrac{dx}{du}du = \dfrac{1}{4x^3}du$

Step 3: $\int \dfrac{2x^3}{\sqrt{1+x^4}}\,dx = \int \left(\dfrac{2x^3}{\sqrt{u}} \times \dfrac{1}{4x^3}\right) du$ (Note: $1 + x^4 = u$)

$\qquad\qquad\qquad\quad = \dfrac{1}{2}\int u^{-\frac{1}{2}}\,du$

$\qquad\qquad\qquad\quad = u^{\frac{1}{2}} + C = \sqrt{1+x^4} + C$

Integration by parts
AQA: P5; EDEXCEL: P3; OCR: P3; WJEC: P3; NICCEA: P3

This method of integration works for some products of functions.
If u and v are functions of x, then:
$\int u\dfrac{dv}{dx}\,dx = uv - \int v\dfrac{du}{dx}\,dx$

Example
Evaluate $\int_0^1 xe^{2x}\,dx$.

Solution
$u = x,\ \dfrac{dv}{dx} = e^{2x} \rightarrow v = \dfrac{1}{2}e^{2x}$

$\int_0^1 xe^{2x}\,dx = \left[x\left(\dfrac{1}{2}e^{2x}\right)\right]_0^1 - \dfrac{1}{2}\int_0^1 e^{2x}\,dx$

$\qquad\qquad\quad = \dfrac{1}{2}e^2 - \dfrac{1}{4}\left[e^{2x}\right]_0^1 = \dfrac{1}{2}e^2 - \dfrac{1}{4}(e^2 - 1) = \dfrac{1}{4}e^2 + \dfrac{1}{4}$

Cartesian and parametric forms

AQA: P5; EDEXCEL: P3; OCR: P3; WJEC: P3; NICCEA: P3

A curve in **cartesian form** is defined in terms of x and y only (e.g. $y = x^2 + 1$, $x^2 - 2xy + y^2 = 1$).

A curve in **parametric form** is defined by expressing x and y in terms of a third variable known as the **parameter**.

Example

Find the cartesian equation of the curve given by the parametric equations $y = 6t^2 + 1$ and $x = 3t$.

Solution

$x = 3t \Rightarrow t = \frac{x}{3}$

Substituting this into $y = 6t^2 + 1$, gives:

$y = 6\left(\frac{x}{3}\right)^2 + 1 = 6\left(\frac{x^2}{9}\right) + 1 = \frac{2x^2}{3} + 1$

Circles

AQA: P3; EDEXCEL: P3, P5

A circle, centre the origin and radius r

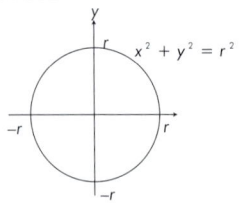

Domain: $-r \leq x \leq r$
Range: $-r \leq y \leq r$

Parametrically $0 \leq \theta \leq 2\pi$
$x = r\cos\theta$, $y = r\sin\theta$

A circle, centre (a, b) and radius r

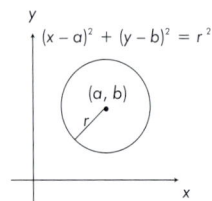

Domain: $a - r \leq x \leq a + r$
Range: $b - r \leq y \leq b + r$

Parametrically $0 \leq \theta \leq 2\pi$
$x = a + r\cos\theta$, $y = b + r\sin\theta$

The ellipse, hyperbola and parabola
AQA: P3; EDEXCEL: P3, P5

Ellipse

$$\frac{x^2}{a^2} + \frac{y^2}{b^2} = 1$$

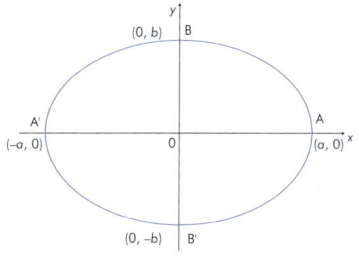

$AA' = 2a$ = major axis
$BB' = 2b$ = minor axis

Parametrically:
$x = a\cos\theta, y = b\sin\theta$

Hyperbola

$$\frac{x^2}{a^2} - \frac{y^2}{b^2} = 1$$

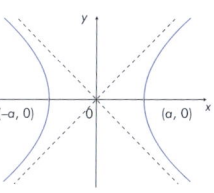

Slant asymptotes:
$y = \frac{b}{a}x$ and $y = -\frac{b}{a}x$

Parametrically:
$x = a\sec\theta, y = b\tan\theta$

Parabola

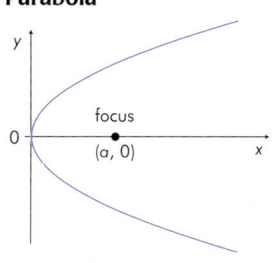

$y^2 = 4ax$
Parametrically:
$x = at^2, y = 2at$

PURE MATHEMATICS — CURVES

Intersection of curves and lines
AQA: P4; EDEXCEL: P3; OCR: P3; WJEC: P2; NICCEA: P3

The intersection of a straight line with a quadratic curve can be simplified to a problem involving the **discriminant and quadratic roots** (i.e. one root, two distinct roots or no real roots).

You need to form a quadratic equation ($y = ax^2 + bx + c$) and examine it to determine whether:

- the line intersects the curve in two points ($b^2 - 4ac > 0$)
- the line is a tangent to the curve ($b^2 - 4ac = 0$)
- the line does not intersect the curve ($b^2 - 4ac < 0$).

Example
Consider the circle $x^2 + y^2 + 4x - 12y - 24 = 0$. Find:

a the centre c and radius r

b the values of k for which the line $y = kx - 2$ is a tangent to the circle.

Solution
a $x^2 + y^2 + 4x - 12y - 24 = 0$
$(x + 2)^2 - 4 + (y - 6)^2 - 36 - 24 = 0$ *Completing the square*
$(x + 2)^2 + (y - 6)^2 = 64$
∴ centre is ($^-2$, 6), radius is 8

b Substituting $y = kx - 2$ into the equation of the circle gives:
$$x^2 + (kx - 2)^2 + 4x - 12(kx - 2) - 24 = 0$$
$$x^2 + k^2x^2 - 4kx + 4 + 4x - 12kx + 24 - 24 = 0$$
$$x^2(k^2 + 1) + x(4 - 16k) + 4 = 0$$
$y = kx - 2$ is a tangent when $b^2 - 4ac = 0$
i.e. $(4 - 16k)^2 - 4 \times (k^2 + 1) \times 4 = 0$
$16 - 128k + 256k^2 - 16k^2 - 16 = 0$
$240k^2 - 128k = 0$
$k(240k - 128) = 0$
i.e. $k = 0$ or $k = \frac{128}{240} = \frac{8}{15}$

PURE MATHEMATICS — CURVES

Implicit differentiation

First derivative   AQA: P5; EDEXCEL: P3; OCR: P3; WJEC: P3; NICCEA: P3
Second derivative   AQA: P5; NICCEA: P3

To differentiate functions given in implicit form follow these basic guidelines:

- $\frac{d}{dx}[y = f(x)] = \frac{dy}{dx} = f'(x)$
- $\frac{d}{dx}[f(y)] = \frac{d}{dy}[f(y)] \times \frac{dy}{dx}$

Example

Find the value of $\frac{dy}{dx}$ for the curve $x^2 + 6xy + 9y^2 = 0$.

Solution

$$2x + 6x\frac{dy}{dx} + 6y + 18y\frac{dy}{dx} = 0$$

$$\frac{dy}{dx}(6x + 18y) = -6y - 2x$$

$$\frac{dy}{dx} = \frac{-2(x + 3y)}{6(x + 3y)} = -\frac{1}{3}$$

Example

Find $\frac{d^2y}{dx^2}$ at the point P(2, 1) on the curve $x^2 - 2y^2 = 2$.

Solution

Differentiating implicitly gives:

$$2x - 4y\frac{dy}{dx} = 0 \Rightarrow \frac{dy}{dx} = \frac{2x}{4y} = \frac{x}{2y}$$

$$2 - \left(4y\frac{d^2y}{dx^2} + \frac{dy}{dx} \times 4\frac{dy}{dx}\right) = 0$$

$$2 - 4y\frac{d^2y}{dx^2} - 4\left(\frac{dy}{dx}\right)^2 = 0$$

At P(2, 1) $y = 1$ and $\frac{dy}{dx} = \frac{2}{2} = 1$.

$$\therefore 2 - 4\frac{d^2y}{dx^2} - 4 = 0$$

$$\frac{d^2y}{dx^2} = -\frac{1}{2}$$

PURE MATHEMATICS — CURVES

Parametric differentiation

First derivative: AQA: P5; EDEXCEL: P3; OCR: P3; WJEC: P3; NICCEA: P3
Second derivative: AQA: P5; NICCEA: P3

If x and y are expressed in terms of parameter t, then:

$$\frac{dy}{dx} = \frac{dy}{dt} \times \frac{dt}{dx}$$

$$\frac{d^2y}{dx^2} = \frac{d^2y}{dt^2} \times \frac{d^2t}{dx^2}$$

Example

A curve is defined parametrically by the equations $x = 2t - 1$ and $y = t^2 + t$.

a Find the slope of the normal at (3, 6).
b Find $\frac{d^2y}{dx^2}$.

Solution

a $x = 2t - 1 \Rightarrow \frac{dx}{dt} = 2 \Rightarrow \frac{dt}{dx} = \frac{1}{2}$

$y = t^2 + t \Rightarrow \frac{dy}{dt} = 2t + 1$

$\frac{dy}{dx} = \frac{dy}{dt} \times \frac{dt}{dx} = (2t + 1) \times \frac{1}{2} = \frac{2t + 1}{2}$

At $x = 3$, $t = 2$ so $\frac{dy}{dx} = \frac{5}{2}$

∴ the gradient of the normal at (3, 6) is $-\frac{2}{5}$.

b $\frac{d^2y}{dx^2} = \frac{d}{dx}\left(\frac{2t + 1}{2}\right)$

$= \frac{d}{dt}\left(\frac{2t + 1}{2}\right) \times \frac{dt}{dx} = 1 \times \frac{1}{2} = \frac{1}{2}$

PURE MATHEMATICS — CURVES

Example

A curve is given parametrically by the equations $x = 1 + \cos t$ and $y = 2\sin^2 t$.

a Find $\frac{dy}{dx}$ at $t = \frac{\pi}{3}$.

b Find the cartesian equation of the curve.

Solution

a $x = 1 + \cos t \Rightarrow \frac{dx}{dt} = -\sin t$

$y = 2\sin^2 t \Rightarrow \frac{dy}{dt} = 4\sin t \cos t$

$\frac{dy}{dx} = \frac{dy}{dt} \times \frac{dt}{dx} = \frac{4\sin t \cos t}{-\sin t} = -4\cos t$

At $t = \frac{\pi}{3}$, $\frac{dy}{dx} = -2$.

b $y = 2\sin^2 t$
  $= 2(1 - \cos^2 t)$
  $= 2(1 - (x-1)^2)$ ($\cos t = x - 1$)
  $= 2(1 - (x^2 - 2x + 1))$
  $= 2(2x - x^2)$
  $= 4x - 2x^2$

Parametric integration
AQA: P5; EDEXCEL: P3

Let $x = f(t)$ and $y = g(t)$ be the parametric equations of a curve. Then the area under the curve is given by:

$$A = \int_{x_1}^{x_2} y\,dx = \int_{t_1}^{t_2} y \frac{dx}{dt}\,dt$$

Example

Use parametric integration to find the area of the region bounded by the ellipse defined by $x = 3\cos t$, $y = 2\sin t$, $0 < t < 2\pi$.

Solution

$$\begin{aligned}
\text{Area} &= \int_0^{2\pi} y\frac{dx}{dt}\,dt = \int_0^{2\pi} 2\sin t(-3\sin t)\,dt \\
&= -6\int_0^{2\pi} \sin^2 t\,dt \\
&= -6\int_0^{2\pi} \tfrac{1}{2}(1 - \cos 2t)\,dt \\
&= -3\left[t - \tfrac{\sin 2t}{2}\right]_0^{2\pi} = -3[(2\pi - 0) - (0 - 0)] = -6\pi
\end{aligned}$$

∴ the area of the ellipse is 6π square units.

The angle between two lines
AQA: P4; EDEXCEL: P3

The acute angle θ between two lines with gradients m_1 and m_2 is given by:

$$\tan\theta = \left|\frac{m_1 - m_2}{1 + m_1 m_2}\right|$$

PURE MATHEMATICS — DIFFERENTIAL EQUATIONS

Solving differential equations
AQA: P5; EDEXCEL: P3; OCR: P3; WJEC: P3; NICCEA: P3

The general form of a first order differential equation is: $\frac{dy}{dx} = f(x, y)$.

If $f(x, y)$ is a function of x only, then the differential equation can be solved by direct integration.

If $f(x, y)$ is in the form $u(x)v(y)$ then the differential equation can be solved by **separating the variables**, where

$$\int \frac{1}{v(y)}\, dy = \int u(x)\, dx$$

Example
Solve $\frac{dy}{dx} = y^2 \cos\left(\frac{x}{2}\right)$ given that $y = 1$ when $x = 0$, expressing your answer in the form $y = f(x)$.

Solution
$\frac{dy}{dx} = y^2 \cos\left(\frac{x}{2}\right)$

$\int \frac{dy}{y^2} = \int \cos\left(\frac{x}{2}\right) dx$

$\int y^{-2} dy = 2\sin\left(\frac{x}{2}\right) + C$

$-y^{-1} = 2\sin\left(\frac{x}{2}\right) + C$

When $y = 1$, $x = 0 \Rightarrow C = {}^{-}1$.

$-\frac{1}{y} = 2\sin\left(\frac{x}{2}\right) - 1$

$$y = \frac{1}{1 - 2\sin\left(\frac{x}{2}\right)}$$

PURE MATHEMATICS   **DIFFERENTIAL EQUATIONS**

Exponential growth and decay

AQA: P4; EDEXCEL: P3; OCR: P2; WJEC: P3

Many quantities, such as population growth and radioactive decay, exhibit exponential growth and decay. There are two main types you need to be familiar with.

- Rate of change of the quantity is proportional to the quantity itself

  $\frac{dy}{dx} = ky \Rightarrow y = Ae^{kx}, \ k > 0$ (*Exponential growth*)

  $\frac{dy}{dx} = -ky \Rightarrow y = Ae^{-kx}, \ k > 0$ (*Exponential decay*)

- Rate of change of the quantity is proportional to the difference between it and a constant c

  $\frac{dy}{dx} = k(y - c) \Rightarrow y = c + Ae^{kx}, \ k > 0$ (*Exponential growth*)

  $\frac{dy}{dx} = -k(y - c) \Rightarrow y = c + Ae^{-kx}, \ k > 0$ (*Exponential decay*)

A common application of growth and decay is Newton's law of cooling.

Newton's law states that the rate at which a body cools in air is proportional to the difference between its temperature T and the constant temperature S of the surrounding air.

$\frac{dT}{dx} = -k(T - S) \Rightarrow T - S = (T_0 - S)e^{-kt}$

where $k > 0$ and T_0 is the initial temperature of the body.

Example

A hard-boiled egg, cooked at 98 °C, is left to cool. After 7 minutes the egg's temperature is 35 °C. Given that the temperature of the surroundings is 22 °C, use Newton's law of cooling to find how much longer it would take for the egg to cool to 25 °C. Give your answer to the nearest minute.

PURE MATHEMATICS   DIFFERENTIAL EQUATIONS

Solution

$T - S = (T_0 - S)e^{-kt} \Rightarrow T = S + (T_0 - S)e^{-kt}$

$T_0 = 98\,°C$, $S = 22\,°C$

$\therefore T = 22 + 76e^{-kt}$

at $t = 7$, $T = 35\,°C$

$\therefore 35 = 22 + 76e^{-7k}$

$e^{-7k} = \frac{13}{76}$

$k = -\frac{1}{7}\ln\frac{13}{76} = 0.2523$

Now, when $T = 25\,°C$:

$25 = 22 + 76e^{-kt}$

$e^{-kt} = \frac{3}{76}$

$\therefore t = -\frac{1}{k}\ln\frac{3}{76} = 12.81 \approx 13$ minutes.

$\therefore$ The egg cools to $25\,°C$ after a further 6 minutes.

PURE MATHEMATICS — VECTORS

Vector notation
AQA: P5; EDEXCEL: P3; OCR: P3; WJEC: P3; NICCEA: P3

The vector from A to B is denoted by $\vec{AB}$. Vectors can also be denoted as single letters (e.g. **a**, **b**, **c**) printed in bold type.

For the magnitude of a vector, use the following notation:
- magnitude of $\vec{AB}$ is denoted by $|\vec{AB}|$
- magnitude of **a** is denoted by $|\mathbf{a}|$ or a.

Components of a vector
AQA: P5; EDEXCEL: P3; OCR: P3; WJEC: P3; NICCEA: P3

Alternatively, you can describe a vector is in terms of its **components** in a specified direction; in two dimensions these are the *x*- and *y*-axes.

For example, the vector **a** in the diagram is denoted by $\begin{pmatrix} 5 \\ -2 \end{pmatrix}$.

It is described as 5 units right and 2 units down.

Operations with vectors
AQA: P5, M1; EDEXCEL: P3; OCR: P3; WJEC: P3, M2; NICCEA: P3

Equal vectors
Two vectors are equal if they have the same **magnitude** and the same **direction**.

Unit vector
The vector $\dfrac{\mathbf{a}}{|\mathbf{a}|}$ acts in the same direction as **a** but has magnitude 1. Such a vector is called a **unit vector**.

PURE MATHEMATICS
VECTORS

The addition of vectors

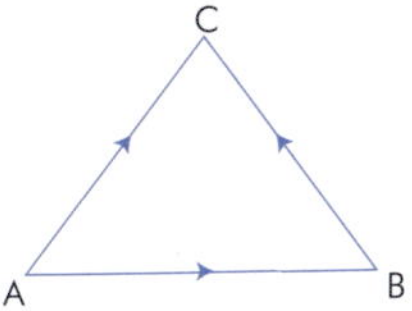

The diagram shows three vectors $\vec{AB}$, $\vec{BC}$ and $\vec{AC}$ such that $\vec{AC} = \vec{AB} + \vec{BC}$.

Vector $\vec{AC}$ is the **resultant**.

Explanation: Suppose you were to walk from A to B ($\vec{AB}$) then from B to C ($\vec{BC}$), following the arrows as shown in the diagram. Now, at point C your position relative to the starting point is given by $\vec{AC}$. Thus $\vec{AB} + \vec{BC} = \vec{AC}$.

Note: The vectors $\vec{AB}$ and $\vec{BC}$ follow on from each other; then $\vec{AC}$ joins the tail of vector $\vec{AB}$ to the head of vector $\vec{BC}$. So the sum or **resultant** of these two vectors has A at its tail and C at its head, i.e. $\vec{AB} + \vec{BC} = \vec{AC}$. This is the **triangle rule**.

The negative of a vector

The negative of vector $\vec{AB}$ is a vector equal in length but opposite in direction to $\vec{AB}$.

$-\vec{AB} = \vec{BA}$

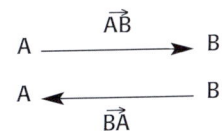

The comutative law

The commutative law holds for addition of vectors.

i.e. $\vec{AB} + \vec{BC} = \vec{BC} + \vec{AB}$

Subtraction of vectors

Given two vectors, $\vec{AB}$ and $\vec{AC}$, as shown in the diagram, you can find their difference as follows.

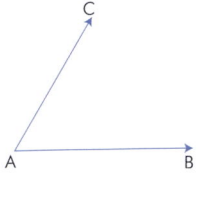

$$\begin{aligned}\vec{AB} - \vec{AC} &= \vec{AB} + -(\vec{AC}) \\ &= \vec{AB} + \vec{CA} \\ &= \vec{CA} + \vec{AB} \quad \text{(Commutative law)} \\ &= \vec{CB} \quad \text{(Triangle law)}\end{aligned}$$

You can show this diagrammatically as follows.

As $-\vec{AC}$ has the opposite direction to $\vec{AC}$, reverse the arrow.

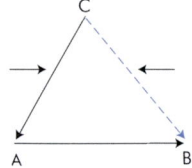

The resultant vector is moving from C to B.
$$\vec{CB} = -\vec{AC} + \vec{AB}$$
$$= \vec{AB} - \vec{AC}$$

Scalar multiplication

For a given vector **a** as shown:

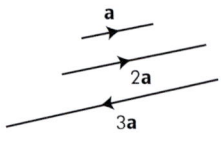

- 2**a** is parallel to **a**, acts in the same direction but is twice as long
- ⁻3**a** is parallel to **a**, acts in the opposite direction and is three times as long.

Example

Vectors **u** and **w** are represented by the sides of triangle ABC as shown, and P is the midpoint of BC. Express **v** in terms of **u** and **w**.

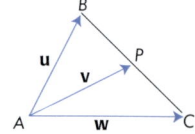

Solution

From the diagram:

$$\vec{AC} + \vec{CP} = \vec{AP}$$

i.e. $\mathbf{w} + \vec{CP} = \mathbf{v}$ $\therefore \vec{CP} = \mathbf{v} - \mathbf{w}$

and $\vec{AP} + \vec{PB} = \vec{AB}$

i.e. $\mathbf{v} + \vec{PB} = \mathbf{u}$ $\therefore \vec{PB} = \mathbf{u} - \mathbf{v}$

But $\vec{CP} = \vec{PB}$ *P is the midpoint of CB.*

$\therefore \mathbf{v} - \mathbf{w} = \mathbf{u} - \mathbf{v}$

$2\mathbf{v} = \mathbf{u} + \mathbf{w}$

$\mathbf{v} = \frac{1}{2}(\mathbf{u} + \mathbf{w})$

Component form

When working in two dimensions, it is often useful to express a vector in terms of two special vectors **i** and **j**. These are **unit vectors** (i.e. their magnitude is 1) perpendicular to each other.

If $\mathbf{r} = a\mathbf{i} + b\mathbf{j}$

then $|\mathbf{r}| = \sqrt{a^2 + b^2}$

and $\tan\theta = \frac{a}{b}$

where θ is the angle made by the vector **r** and the positive direction of the x-axis.

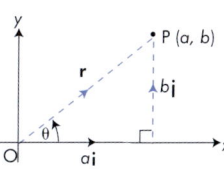

Position vectors

The position vector of a point P is the vector $\overrightarrow{OP}$ where O is the origin.

If P has coordinates (a, b) then its position vector is given by $r = a\mathbf{i} + b\mathbf{j}$.

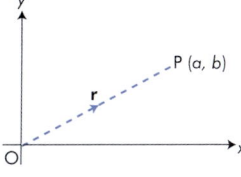

Adding and subtracting vectors algebraically

AQA: P5; EDEXCEL: P3; OCR: P3; WJEC: P3; NICCEA: P3

You can add and subtract vectors algebraically, simply by adding or subtracting their components.

If $\mathbf{a} = \binom{a_1}{a_2} = a_1\mathbf{i} + a_2\mathbf{j}$ and $\mathbf{b} = \binom{b_1}{b_2} = b_1\mathbf{i} + b_2\mathbf{j}$, then:

$\mathbf{a} + \mathbf{b} = \binom{a_1}{a_2} + \binom{b_1}{b_2} = \binom{a_1 + b_1}{a_2 + b_2} = (a_1 + b_1)\mathbf{i} + (a_2 + b_2)\mathbf{j}$

$\mathbf{a} - \mathbf{b} = \binom{a_1}{a_2} - \binom{b_1}{b_2} = \binom{a_1 - b_1}{a_2 - b_2} = (a_1 - b_1)\mathbf{i} + (a_2 - b_2)\mathbf{j}$

The scalar product

AQA: P5; EDEXCEL: P3; OCR: P3; WJEC: P3; NICCEA: P3

Given two vectors **a** and **b** acting at an angle θ to each other, then the **scalar product** (or **dot product**) of **a** and **b** is defined as:

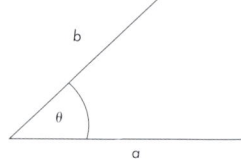

$\mathbf{a} \cdot \mathbf{b} = |\mathbf{a}||\mathbf{b}|\cos\theta$

If two vectors are parallel, $\theta = 0$ and
$\mathbf{a} \cdot \mathbf{b} = |\mathbf{a}||\mathbf{b}|\cos 0 = |\mathbf{a}||\mathbf{b}|$

If two vectors are perpendicular, $\theta = 90°$ and $\mathbf{a} \cdot \mathbf{b} = |\mathbf{a}||\mathbf{b}|\cos 90° = 0$

Scalar product and components

For two vectors $\mathbf{a} = a_1\mathbf{i} + a_2\mathbf{j}$ and $\mathbf{b} = b_1\mathbf{i} + b_2\mathbf{j}$ expressed in component form the scalar product is given by:

$$\mathbf{a} \cdot \mathbf{b} = (a_1\mathbf{i} + a_2\mathbf{j}) \cdot (b_1\mathbf{i} + b_2\mathbf{j}) = \begin{pmatrix} a_1 \\ a_2 \end{pmatrix} \cdot \begin{pmatrix} b_1 \\ b_2 \end{pmatrix} = a_1 b_1 + a_2 b_2$$

Note: $\mathbf{a} \cdot \mathbf{b} = \mathbf{b} \cdot \mathbf{a}$, $\mathbf{i} \cdot \mathbf{i} = \mathbf{j} \cdot \mathbf{j} = \mathbf{k} \cdot \mathbf{k} = 1$, $\mathbf{i} \cdot \mathbf{j} = \mathbf{j} \cdot \mathbf{k} = \mathbf{k} \cdot \mathbf{i} = 0$

The vector equation of a line

AQA: P5; EDEXCEL: P3; OCR: P3; WJEC: P3; NICCEA: P3

The vector equation of a line through a point A with position vector **a** and parallel to vector **b** is given by:

$\mathbf{r} = \mathbf{a} + t\mathbf{b}$, where t is a scalar parameter.

Note: **b** is the **direction vector** of the line. The vector equation of a line through points A and B with position vectors **a** and **b** is given by:

$\mathbf{r} = \mathbf{a} + t(\mathbf{b} - \mathbf{a}) = (1 - t)\mathbf{a} + t\mathbf{b}$, where t is a scalar parameter.

Angles between two lines

To find the angle between two lines, find the angle between their direction vectors.

PURE MATHEMATICS — VECTORS

Vectors in three dimensions
AQA: P5; EDEXCEL: P3; OCR: P3; WJEC: P3; NICCEA: P3

Two vectors in three dimensions are written as:

$\mathbf{a} = a_1\mathbf{i} + a_2\mathbf{j} + a_3\mathbf{k}$ and $\mathbf{b} = b_1\mathbf{i} + b_2\mathbf{j} + b_3\mathbf{k}$

The magnitude of $\mathbf{a}$ is $\mathbf{a} = \sqrt{a_1^2 + a_2^2 + a_3^2}$

The scalar product of the two vectors is:

$\mathbf{a} \cdot \mathbf{b} = a_1b_1 + a_2b_2 + a_3b_3$

Note: The sections on the scalar product and the vector equation of a line apply equally to vectors in three dimensions.

Pairs of lines
AQA: P5; OCR: P3; WJEC: P3

In two dimensions, two lines are either **parallel** or they **intersect**.

In three dimensions, two lines are parallel or they intersect or they are **skew**.

Skew lines are straight lines that are not parallel and do not intersect; they are like the paths of two aircraft flying at different heights in different directions.

Two lines are parallel if their **direction vectors** are multiples of each other.

Two lines $\mathbf{r}_1 = \mathbf{a} + t\mathbf{b}$ and $\mathbf{r}_2 = \mathbf{a} + s\mathbf{b}$ intersect if there are unique solutions for s and t such that $\mathbf{r}_1 = \mathbf{r}_2$.

Example

Which of the following pairs of lines intersect? For those that do, find the point of intersection and the angle between the lines.

1. $\mathbf{r}_1 = \mathbf{i} - \mathbf{k} + t(\mathbf{i} + 3\mathbf{j} + 4\mathbf{k})$ and
   $\mathbf{r}_2 = -5\mathbf{i} - 7\mathbf{j} - 7\mathbf{k} + s(4\mathbf{i} + \mathbf{j} - 2\mathbf{k})$
2. $\mathbf{r}_1 = -3\mathbf{i} + \mathbf{j} + 4\mathbf{k} + t(-\mathbf{i} + 2\mathbf{k})$ and
   $\mathbf{r}_2 = -2\mathbf{i} + 2\mathbf{j} + \mathbf{k} + s(2\mathbf{i} + \mathbf{j} - \mathbf{k})$

Solution

a $r_1 = r_2 \Rightarrow i - k + t(i + 3j + 4k) = -5i - 7j - 7k + s(4i + j - 2k)$

ie. $(1 + t)i + (3t)j + (4t - 1)k = (4s - 5)i + (s - 7)j + (^-7 - 2s)k$

Equating coefficients:
$1 + t = 4s - 5$ (1)
$3t = s - 7$ (2)
$4t - 1 = {^-7} - 2s$ (3)

Solving (1) and (2) simultaneously gives: $s = 1$ and $t = -2$.
Check to see whether these satisfy (3).

LHS $= {^-8} - 1 = {^-9}$ and RHS $= {^-7} - 2 = {^-9}$

$\therefore s = 1$ and $t = {^-2}$ satisfy all three equations.
The lines r_1 and r_2 intersect.

Thus the position vector of the point of intersection is given by:

$r = i - k - 2(i + 3j + 4k) = -i - 6j - 9k = \begin{pmatrix} -1 \\ -6 \\ -9 \end{pmatrix}$

The angle between the two lines is given by:

$\cos \theta = \dfrac{a \cdot b}{|a| \, |b|}$, where a and b represent the direction vectors of r_1 and r_2.

$a \cdot b = \begin{pmatrix} 1 \\ 3 \\ 4 \end{pmatrix} \cdot \begin{pmatrix} 4 \\ 1 \\ -2 \end{pmatrix} = 1 \times 4 + 3 \times 1 - 4 \times 2 = -1$

$|a| = \sqrt{1^2 + 3^2 + 4^2} = \sqrt{26}$, $|b| = \sqrt{4^2 + 1^2 + {-2}^2} = \sqrt{21}$

$\cos \theta = \dfrac{-1}{\sqrt{26}\sqrt{21}} = -0.0427 \ldots \Rightarrow \theta = 92.45°$ (2 d.p.)

b $r_1 = r_2 \Rightarrow -3i + j + 4k + t(-i + 2k) = -2i + 2j + k + s(2i + j - k)$

i.e. $({^-3} - t)i + j + (4 + 2t)k = (2s - 2)i + (s + 2)j + (1 - s)k$

Equating coefficients:
${^-3} - t = 2s - 2$ (1)
$1 = s + 2$ (2)
$4 + 2t = 1 - s$ (3)

Solving (1) and (2) simultaneously gives: $s = {^-1}$ and $t = 1$.
Check to see whether these satisfy (3).

LHS = 4 + 2 = 6 and RHS = 1 + 1 = 2

∴ $s = {}^-1$ and $t = 1$ do not satisfy all three equations.
The lines $\mathbf{r}_1$ and $\mathbf{r}_2$ do not intersect.

Planes

AQA: P5

The vector equation of a plane through a point A with position vector $\mathbf{a}$ and perpendicular to a vector $\mathbf{n}$ is given by:

$$(\mathbf{r} - \mathbf{a}) \cdot \mathbf{n} = 0 \Rightarrow \mathbf{r} \cdot \mathbf{n} = \mathbf{a} \cdot \mathbf{n}$$

To express in cartesian form, substitute $\mathbf{r} = x\mathbf{i} + y\mathbf{j} + z\mathbf{k}$.

The angle between two planes is given by:

$$\frac{\mathbf{n}_1 \cdot \mathbf{n}_2}{|\mathbf{n}_1|\,|\mathbf{n}_2|} = \cos\theta$$

where $\mathbf{n}_1$ and $\mathbf{n}_2$ are the normal vectors to the plane.

PURE MATHEMATICS — **NUMERICAL METHODS**

Newton–Raphson method
AQA: P4; NICCEA: P3

The Newton-Raphson method is used for approximating the roots of an equation.

If x_1 is an approximation to the roof $f(x) = 0$, a better approximation x_2 is obtained as follows:

$$x_2 = x_1 - \frac{f(x_1)}{f'(x_1)}$$

Numerical integration
AQA: P5

There are three methods that can be used for approximating the value of an integral that is too difficult or impossible to evaluate.

They are commonly used to find the area under a curve.

Simpson's rule

$$\int_a^b f(x)\,dx \approx \frac{h}{3}\{y_0 + y_n + 2(y_2 + y_4 + \ldots) + 4(y_1 + y_3 + \ldots)\}$$

where h is the common width of the strips.

You need an even number of strips.

Note: Make sure you do not mix up the 2 and 4 in the formula. To remind you, just remember FOTE (**F**our **O**dd **T**wo **E**ven).

Mid-ordinate rule

$$\int_a^b f(x)\,dx \approx h(y_{0.5} + y_{1.5} + \ldots + y_{n-0.5})$$

where h is the common width of the strip.

Trapezium rule
NICCEA: P2

$$\int_a^b f(x)\,dx \approx \frac{h}{2}\{y_0 + y_n + 2(y_1 + y_2 + \ldots + y_{n-1})\}$$

where h is the common width of the strips.

MECHANICS   PROJECTILES

The basic formulae
AQA: M1; EDEXCEL: M2; OCR: M2; WJEC: M2; NICCEA: M2

In the A2 course, the study of projectile motion involves analysing the equations of motion of a particle projected upwards at angle α to the horizontal.

Ignoring air resistance, it is assumed that the only force acting on the particle is its weight vertically downwards and therefore that the horizontal component of velocity is constant.

You need to analyse the horizontal and vertical components of the motion separately.

A particle projected with velocity v at angle α to the horizontal (as shown) has the following features.

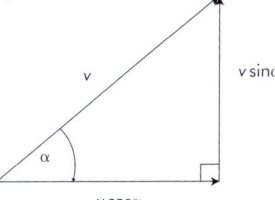

Horizontal acceleration $= 0$	Vertical acceleration $= -g$
Horizontal velocity $= v\cos\alpha$ (remains constant)	Vertical velocity $= u + at$ $= v\sin\alpha - gt$
Horizontal displacement $= ut + \frac{1}{2}at^2$ $= vt\cos\alpha$	Vertical displacement $= ut + \frac{1}{2}at^2$ $= vt\sin\alpha - \frac{1}{2}gt^2$

Time of flight (*T*)

This is the time for which the particle has been in motion when the vertical displacement is zero (i.e. when the particle returns to the horizontal plane).

$vt\sin\alpha - \frac{1}{2}gt^2 = 0$

$t(v\sin\alpha - \frac{1}{2}gt) = 0$

$\therefore t = 0$ or $t = \frac{2v\sin\alpha}{g}$

$\therefore T = \frac{2v\sin\alpha}{g}$

MECHANICS — PROJECTILES

Horizontal range (*R*)

The horizontal range is found by substituting the time of flight (*T*) into the horizontal component of velocity.

$R = vT\cos\alpha = v\left(\frac{2v\sin\alpha}{g}\right)\cos\alpha = \frac{2v^2\sin\alpha\cos\alpha}{g}$

$R = \frac{v^2\sin 2\alpha}{g}$

Note: The maximum range, R_{max}, occurs when $\sin 2\alpha = 1$ i.e. when $\alpha = 45°$.

Maximum height (*H*)

The maximum height is attained when the vertical component of the velocity is zero.

$v\sin\alpha - gt = 0$, when $t = \frac{v\sin\alpha}{g}$

Substituting this into $vt\sin\alpha - \frac{1}{2}gt^2$ gives:

$H = v\left(\frac{v\sin\alpha}{g}\right)\sin\alpha - \frac{1}{2}g\left(\frac{v\sin\alpha}{g}\right)^2 = \frac{v^2\sin^2\alpha}{2g}$

$\therefore H = \frac{v^2\sin^2\alpha}{2g}$

Position vector

The displacement of the particle may also be expressed as a position vector in terms of its horizontal and vertical components of displacement.

$\mathbf{r} = vt\cos\alpha\mathbf{i} + (vt\sin\alpha - \frac{1}{2}gt^2)\mathbf{j}$

MECHANICS — PROJECTILES

Cartesian equation of the path
AQA: M1; OCR: M2; NICCEA: M2

The path of a projectile may be expressed in terms of x and y by considering its horizontal and vertical displacements.

Horizontally: $x = vt\cos\alpha \Rightarrow t = \dfrac{x}{v\cos\alpha}$ (1)

Vertically: $y = vt\sin\alpha - \dfrac{1}{2}gt^2$ (2)

substituting from (1) into (2) gives:

$y = v\left(\dfrac{x}{v\cos\alpha}\right)\sin\alpha - \dfrac{1}{2}g\left(\dfrac{x}{v\cos\alpha}\right)^2$

$ = x\tan\alpha - \dfrac{gx^2}{2v^2}\left(\dfrac{1}{\cos^2\alpha}\right)$

$ = x\tan\alpha - \dfrac{gx^2}{2v^2}\sec^2\alpha$

$y = x\tan\alpha - \dfrac{gx^2}{2v^2}(1 + \tan^2\alpha)$

Note: This is the cartesian equation of a parabola, it is also known as the **trajectory formula**.

MECHANICS — KINEMATICS AND DYNAMICS

Velocity and acceleration

AQA: M2, M3; EDEXCEL: M3; OCR: M3; WJEC: M2, M3; NICCEA: M2

Kinematics is the study of the motion of a particle in terms of its displacement, velocity and acceleration, but without considering any forces acting to produce the motion. You can find velocities and accelerations by differentiating expressions for displacement. Displacements and velocities can also be found by **integrating** expressions for acceleration.

$$v = \frac{dx}{dt} = \dot{x} \qquad a = \frac{dv}{dt} = \frac{d^2x}{dt^2} = \ddot{x}$$

$$x = \int v\,dt + c \qquad v = \int a\,dt + c$$

Differentiate: $x \to v \to a$
Integrate: $a \to v \to x$

An important formula linking a and v with respect to x is given by:

$$a = \frac{dv}{dt} = \frac{dv}{dx} \times \frac{dx}{dt} \qquad \text{(Using the chain rule)}$$

$$= v\frac{dv}{dx} \qquad \left(\text{Since } v = \frac{dx}{dt}\right)$$

Example

A particle starts its motion at the origin and moves in a straight line with velocity $(5 + 2e^{-x})$ m s^{-1}. Find its acceleration at the origin.

Solution

$$a = v\frac{dv}{dx} = (5 + 2e^{-x}) \times \frac{d}{dx}(5 + 2e^{-x})$$

$$= (5 + 2e^{-x}) \times -2e^{-x} = -10e^{-x} - 4e^{-2x}$$

At $x = 0$, $a = -14$ m s^{-2}.

Distance/speed versus displacement/velocity

AQA: M3; EDEXCEL: M2; OCR: M1; WJEC: M2; NICCEA: M2

You need to know the distinction between distance/speed and displacement/velocity.

Distance and speed are **scalar** measures, which means that they have **magnitude** (size) but not direction. In other words, distance and speed are always taken to be positive.

MECHANICS — KINEMATICS AND DYNAMICS

Displacement and velocity are **vector** measures, which means that they have both **magnitude and direction**.

Displacement and velocity may be positive or negative, depending on the direction of the movement. For linear motion, movement to the right is taken to be positive, and movement to the left is taken to be negative.

Calculus in two and three dimensions
AQA: M2; EDEXCEL: M2; WJEC: M2; NICCEA: M2

The principles used in calculus in one dimension can be extended to two or three dimensions. Vectors for position **r**, velocity **v** and acceleration **a** are linked through differentiation and integration.

Differentiation

$\mathbf{r} = x\mathbf{i} + y\mathbf{j} + z\mathbf{k}$

$\mathbf{v} = \dot{\mathbf{r}} = \frac{dx}{dt}\mathbf{i} + \frac{dy}{dt}\mathbf{j} + \frac{dz}{dt}\mathbf{k}$

$\mathbf{a} = \dot{\mathbf{v}} = \ddot{\mathbf{r}} = \frac{d^2x}{dt^2}\mathbf{i} + \frac{d^2y}{dt^2}\mathbf{j} + \frac{d^2z}{dt^2}\mathbf{k}$

Integration

$\mathbf{v} = \int \mathbf{a}\, dt + c$

$\mathbf{r} = \int \mathbf{v}\, dt + c$

Note: In two dimensions the **k** term is simply omitted.

Example

A particle P has velocity $\mathbf{v} = t^2\mathbf{i} + (5t - 4)\mathbf{j}$ m s^{-1} at time t seconds.

Given P is initially at the point $-3\mathbf{i}$ metres with respect to the origin O. Find:

a the acceleration of P at time t seconds

b the times when P is moving parallel to vector $\mathbf{i} + \mathbf{j}$

c the distance OP, to 2 decimal places, when $t = 6$.

Solution

a $\mathbf{a} = \dot{\mathbf{v}} = 2t\mathbf{i} + 5\mathbf{j}$ m s^{-2}

b $\mathbf{v} = t^2\mathbf{i} + (5t - 4)\mathbf{j}$

Now, P moves parallel to vector $\mathbf{i} + \mathbf{j}$ when **v** is of the form $c(\mathbf{i} + \mathbf{j})$.

i.e. when $t^2 = 5t - 4 \Rightarrow t^2 - 5t + 4 = 0$
$$(t-4)(t-1) = 0$$
$$t = 1 \text{ or } t = 4$$

At $t = 1$, $\mathbf{v} = \mathbf{i} + \mathbf{j}$ and at $t = 4$, $\mathbf{v} = 16(\mathbf{i} + \mathbf{j})$.

∴ P is moving parallel to vector $\mathbf{i} + \mathbf{j}$ at $t = 4$ and at $t = 1$.

c $\mathbf{r} = \int \mathbf{v} \, dt$
$= \int (t^2 \mathbf{i} + (5t - 4)\mathbf{j}) \, dt$
$= \frac{t^3 \mathbf{i}}{3} + \left(\frac{5t^2}{2} - 4t\right)\mathbf{j} + c$

At $t = 0$, $\mathbf{r} = -3\mathbf{i} \Rightarrow c = -3\mathbf{i}$

∴ $\mathbf{r} = \frac{t^3 \mathbf{i}}{3} + \left(\frac{5t^2}{2} - 4t\right)\mathbf{j} - 3\mathbf{i}$
$= \left(\frac{t^3 \mathbf{i}}{3} - 3\right)\mathbf{i} + \left(\frac{5t^2}{2} - 4t\right)\mathbf{j}$

At $t = 6$, $\mathbf{r} = 69\mathbf{i} + 66\mathbf{j}$

Distance OP $= |\mathbf{r}| = \sqrt{69^2 + 66^2} = 95.48$ m (2 d.p.)

Dynamics

AQA: M2; EDEXCEL: M3; OCR: M3; WJEC: M2, M3; NICCEA: M2

Dynamics is the study of the motion of a particle in response to the forces acting upon it. These problems frequently require you to apply Newton's second law ($F = ma$) to produce an expression for the acceleration of the object being considered.

If acceleration is a function of t, then the acceleration can be equated to $\ddot{x}$ or $\dot{v}$ and integrated. However, if the acceleration is a function of x or v, then acceleration can be equated to $v\frac{dv}{dx}$ and integrated using the method of **separation of variables**.

Example

A particle of mass 0.5 kg moves away from the origin O under the action of a force of magnitude $3\sqrt{x+1}$ N directed towards O, where $OP = x$ metres. When $x = 3$ the speed of P is 4 m s^{-1}. Find x when P is brought to rest.

Solution

$F = ma$: $-3\sqrt{x+1} = 0.5v\dfrac{dv}{dx}$

$\int -3(x+1)^{\frac{1}{2}} dx = \int 0.5v\, dv$

$-2(x+1)^{\frac{3}{2}} + c = \dfrac{v^2}{4}$

When $x = 3$, $v = 4$ $\therefore c = 4 + 2(4)^{\frac{3}{2}} = 20$

$\therefore v^2 = 80 - 8(x+1)^{\frac{3}{2}}$

P is brought to rest when $v = 0$,

i.e. $80 = 8(x+1)^{\frac{3}{2}} \Rightarrow 10 = (x+1)^{\frac{3}{2}} \Rightarrow x = 3.641\ldots$

The particle P is brought to rest when $x = 3.64$ m (2 d.p.).

| MECHANICS | ENERGY, WORK AND POWER |

Energy
AQA: M2; EDEXCEL: M2; OCR: M2; WJEC: M2, MS; NICCEA: M2

There are two kinds of mechanical energy: **kinetic energy** (KE) and **potential energy** (PE).

Kinetic energy is the energy of a moving object. Its value is determined by the speed with which the object is moving, and its mass.

$KE = \frac{1}{2}mv^2$

The units of energy are joules, J, when v is in $m\,s^{-1}$ and m is in kg.

An object has potential energy if it is in a position where it can do work. An object has **gravitational potential energy** when it has been raised to a certain height (h) above ground level. Gravitational potential energy is given by:

$PE = mgh$

The total mechanical energy of an object represents the sum of is KE and PE.

The principle of **conservation of energy** states that the total mechanical energy of an object remains constant provided no other external force other than gravity acts on the object.

Work
AQA: M2; EDEXCEL: M2; OCR: M2; WJEC: M2, MS; NICCEA: M2

When there has been a change in the energy of a system or object, then work has been done to bring about the change.

Change in KE = work done = Fs

where F is the resultant force that is moving the object through distance s. The unit of work is the **joule** (J).

Note: If the speed of an object increases from u to v, then the change in KE is given by:

$KE = \frac{1}{2}mv^2 - \frac{1}{2}mu^2$

MECHANICS — ENERGY, WORK AND POWER

Work in two dimensions

When a force is applied at an angle to the direction of motion, then only that component which is in line with the direction of motion contributes to the work done.

If a force F acts at an angle θ to the direction of motion, then:

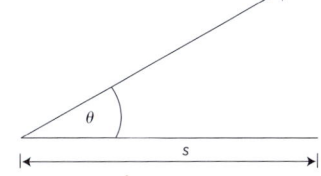

Example

An object of mass 2 kg slides down a 5 m slope inclined at 30° to the horizontal. Its speed at the bottom of the slope is 4 m s^{-1}. Find the work done by gravity and the work done against friction.

Solution

$$\begin{aligned}\text{Work done by gravity} &= Fs\cos\theta \\ &= mgs\cos\theta \\ &= 2 \times 9.8 \times 5 \times \cos 60° \\ &= 49 \text{ J}\end{aligned}$$

$$\begin{aligned}\text{Work done against friction} &= \text{work done by gravity} - \text{final kinetic energy} \\ &= 49 - \tfrac{1}{2}mv^2 \\ &= 49 - \tfrac{1}{2} \times 2 \times 4^2 \\ &= 33 \text{ J}\end{aligned}$$

MECHANICS — ENERGY, WORK AND POWER

Power
AQA: M2; EDEXCEL: M2; OCR: M2; WJEC: M2; NICCEA: M2

Power is the rate at which work is done. It is given by:

$P = Fv$ or $P = \dfrac{W}{t}$

where F is the force, in newtons, and s is the speed, in m s^{-1}.

It is measured in **watts** (W) where $1\text{ W} = 1\text{ J s}^{-1}$.

Example

A car can reach a top speed of 180 km h^{-1} on horizontal ground against resistance forces of 1500 N. Find the power generated by the car at top speed.

Solution

$P = Fv$, where v is in m s^{-1}.

$180\text{ km h}^{-1} = \dfrac{180 \times 1000}{60 \times 60} = 50\text{ m s}^{-1}$

Power at top speed $= 1500 \times 50$
$= 75\,000$ W
$= 75$ kW

MECHANICS — MOMENTUM AND COLLISIONS

Momentum

AQA: M1; EDEXCEL: M2; OCR: M1, M3; WJEC: M2; NICCEA: M1

The momentum of a particle is a vector quantity.

Momentum = $m\mathbf{v}$

If two particles collide, then the principle of conservation of momentum states:

the total momentum before impact = the total momentum after impact

$m_1\mathbf{u}_1 + m_2\mathbf{u}_2 = m_1\mathbf{v}_1 + m_2\mathbf{v}_2$

For your A2 course you must be capable of working with momentum in two dimensions.

Impulse

EDEXCEL: M2; OCR: M3; WJEC: M2; NICCEA: M1

Impulse = change in momentum $\mathbf{I} = \mathbf{F}t = m\mathbf{v} - m\mathbf{u} = m(\mathbf{v} - \mathbf{u})$

Example

A particle A of mass 3 kg moving with velocity $4\mathbf{i} + 2\mathbf{j}$ m s^{-1} collides with another particle B of mass 1 kg, which is at rest. After the impact both objects move together with the same speed of v m s^{-1}.

a Find the speed after impact.

b Find the magnitude of the impulse exerted on B by A during impact.

Solution

a $m_1\mathbf{u}_1 + m_2\mathbf{u}_2 = m_1\mathbf{v}_1 + m_2\mathbf{v}_2$

where $m_1 = 3$, $\mathbf{u}_1 = 4\mathbf{i} + 2\mathbf{j}$, $m_2 = 1$, $u_2 = 0$

$\mathbf{v}_1 = \mathbf{v}_2 = \mathbf{v}$

i.e. $3(4\mathbf{i} + 2\mathbf{j}) + 1 \times 0 = 3\mathbf{v} + \mathbf{v}$

$12\mathbf{i} + 6\mathbf{j} = 4\mathbf{v}$

$\mathbf{v} = 3\mathbf{i} + 1.5\mathbf{j}$

b Impulse $= m(\mathbf{v} - \mathbf{u}) = m_2(\mathbf{v} - 0) = 3\mathbf{i} + 1.5\mathbf{j}$

Mechanics — Momentum and Collisions

Area under a force–time graph
EDEXCEL: M2; WJEC: M2

A relationship exists between the area under a force–time graph and the impulse.

$$\int_{t_1}^{t_2} F(t)\, dt = mv - mu \quad \text{or} \quad I = \int_{t_1}^{t_2} F(t)\, dt$$

This result allows you to find the impulse when a variable force acts. When the force is constant it reduces to $Ft = I$.

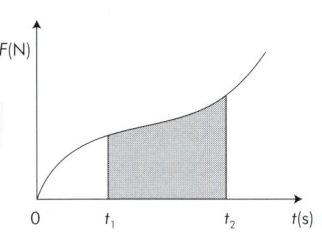

The coefficient of restitution
EDEXCEL: M2; OCR: M2

Newton's experimental law states that when two objects collide, their speed of separation and speed of approach are related to each other by a constant e called the **coefficient of restitution**.

Speed of separation = $e \times$ speed of approach, $0 \leq e \leq 1$

The constant e depends on the type of object and the surface it moves on.

The solution to these problems is found by solving the simultaneous equations for the conservation of momentum and Newton's experimental law.

There are essentially three types of problems you can encounter.

Type 1: Particles travelling in the same direction.

Conservation of momentum:

$m_1 u_1 + m_2 u_2 = m_1 v_1 + m_2 v_2$

Newton's law: $v_2 - v_1 = e(u_1 - u_2)$

MECHANICS — MOMENTUM AND COLLISIONS

Type 2: Particles travelling in opposite directions. There are two scenarios.

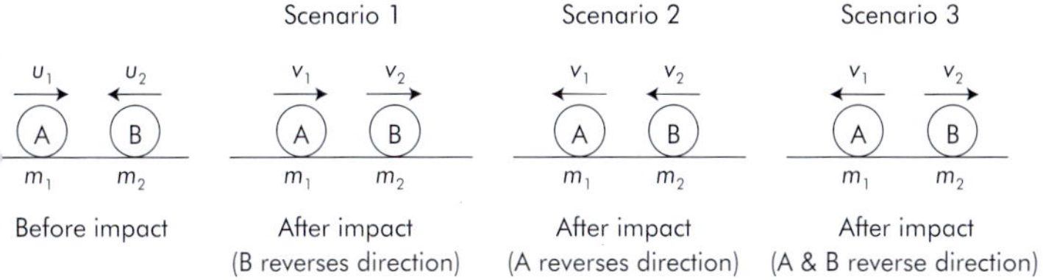

Scenario 1 — After impact (B reverses direction)
Scenario 2 — After impact (A reverses direction)
Scenario 3 — After impact (A & B reverse direction)

Scenario 1: Conservation of momentum:
$m_1u_1 - m_2u_2 = m_1v_1 + m_2v_2$

Newton's law: $v_2 - v_1 = e(u_1 + u_2)$

Scenario 2: Conservation of momentum:
$m_1u_1 - m_2u_2 = -m_1v_1 - m_2v_2$

Newton's law: $v_1 - v_2 = e(u_1 + u_2)$

Scenario 3: Conservation of momentum:
$m_1u_1 - m_2u_2 = m_2v_2 - m_1v_1$

Newton's law: $v_1 + v_2 = e(u_1 + u_2)$

Type 3: One particle is stationary.

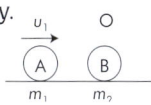

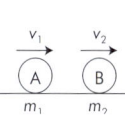

Conservation of momentum:
$m_1u_1 = m_1v_1 + m_2v_2$

Newton's law: $v_2 - v_1 = eu_1$

Collisions in two dimensions

OCR: M3

You will need to be able to solve problems involving the oblique impact of two smooth spheres of equal size on a smooth surface.

There are two important features you need to know.

- The component of velocity of either sphere perpendicular to their line of centres (i.e. $C_A C_B$) remains unchanged.

  i.e. $u_1 \sin \theta = v_1 \sin \alpha$

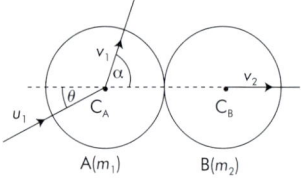

- Along the line $C_A C_B$ the equations normally used for a direct impact still apply.

  i.e. $m_1 u_1 \cos \theta = m_1 v_1 \cos \alpha + m_2 v_2$

MECHANICS — MOMENTS AND EQUILIBRIUM

Equilibrium

AQA: M1; EDEXCEL: M2, M3; OCR: M2; WJEC: M1, M3; NICCEA: M1

For a rigid body to be in equilibrium it must satisfy the following conditions.

- The resultant force must be zero.
- The total moment about any point must be zero.

Note: From the AS course, you should recall that the moment of a force is the product of the distance and the component of the force perpendicular to the defined distance, $Fd\sin\theta$.

Example

The lever shown is at rest and pivoted at O. A force of 30 N is applied at P. A rope is attached at Q. Given PQ = 2.5 m and OQ = 2 m, find:

a the tension in the rope

b the magnitude of the force exerted on the lever by the pivot at O.

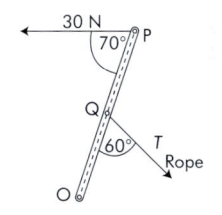

Solution

a As the lever is in equilibrium, the total moment about O is zero.

M(O) gives: $30\sin 70° \times 4.5 = T\sin 60° \times 2$

$T = 73.2$ N (1 d.p.)

b As the lever is in equilibrium the resultant force must be zero.

Horizontal component = $73.2\cos 50° - 30 = 17.1$ N

Vertical component = $73.2\cos 40° = 56.1$ N

$\therefore$ Resultant force = $\sqrt{(17.1)^2 + (56.1)^2}$

= 58.6 N

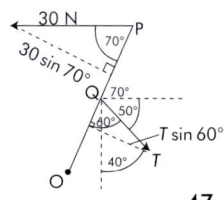

MECHANICS — MOMENTS AND EQUILIBRIUM

Leaning ladders

AQA: M1; EDEXCEL: M3; OCR: M2; WJEC: M1, M3; NICCEA: M1

A common application of moments, equilibrium and the theory of friction involves a ladder leaning against a wall and possibly supporting a load at some point.

Example

A uniform ladder, of mass m kg and length $2a$, has one end on rough, horizontal ground and the other against a smooth, vertical wall.

A man of mass $6m$ kg stands halfway up the ladder and the ladder is in equilibrium. If the angle between the ladder and the horizontal is 60°, show that:

$$\mu \geq \frac{1}{2\sqrt{3}} \qquad (\mu \text{ is the coefficient of friction})$$

Solution

The diagram shows the forces acting on the ladder.

For the resultant force to be zero, you must have:

vertically: $\quad R = 6mg \qquad$ (1)

vorizontally: $\quad F = s \qquad$ (2)

Taking moments at A gives:

$M(A)$: $s \times 2a \sin 60° = 6mg \times a \cos 60°$

$\qquad s \times \sqrt{3}a = 3mga$

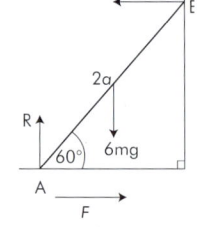

$\qquad s = \sqrt{3}mg \qquad$ (3)

From (2) and (3): $F = \sqrt{3}mg$

As the ladder remains at rest, the friction inequality $F \leq \mu R$ can be used with the above values.

$\qquad F \leq \mu R$

$\sqrt{3}mg \leq \mu \times 6mg$

$\qquad \mu \geq \frac{\sqrt{3}}{6} = \frac{1}{2\sqrt{3}}$ as required.

MECHANICS — CENTRE OF MASS

Centre of mass of a triangle
AQA: M1; EDEXCEL: M2; OCR: M2; WJEC: M1; NICCEA: M3

The centre of mass of a triangle is the point of intersection of any two medians; they meet $\frac{1}{3}$ of the way up from the side to the vertex.

Centre of mass of a system of particles
AQA: M1; EDEXCEL: M2; OCR: M2; WJEC: M1; NICCEA: M3

If all the particles lie on a straight line, then the distance of the centre of mass from O ($\bar{x}$) is given by:

$\bar{x} = \frac{1}{M} \sum_{i=1}^{n} m_i x_i$, where M is the total mass.

If the particles lie in two dimensions, then the distance of the centre of mass from O ($\bar{x}, \bar{y}$) is given by:

$\bar{x} = \frac{1}{M} \sum_{i=1}^{n} m_i x_i$ and $\bar{y} = \frac{1}{M} \sum_{i=1}^{n} m_i y_i$, where M is the total mass.

If unit vectors are introduced, so that each particle has its position given by $\mathbf{r}_i = x_i \mathbf{i} + y_i \mathbf{j}$ then the position of the centre of mass is:

$\mathbf{r} = \bar{x}\mathbf{i} + \bar{y}\mathbf{j} = (\frac{1}{M} \sum_{i=1}^{n} m_i x_i)\mathbf{i} + (\frac{1}{M} \sum_{i=1}^{n} m_i y_i)\mathbf{j}$

Example

Masses of 3 kg, 4 kg and 8 kg are positioned as shown in the diagram.

Find the coordinates of the centre of mass of the system.

Solution

$M = 3 + 4 + 8 = 15$

$\bar{x} = \frac{1}{15} \sum_{i=1}^{3} x_i m_i = \frac{1}{15}(1 \times 3 + 6 \times 4 + 7 \times 8) = 5.53$ to 2 d.p.

$\bar{y} = \frac{1}{15} \sum_{i=1}^{3} y_i m_i = \frac{1}{15}(2 \times 3 + 1 \times 4 + 5 \times 8) = 3.33$ to 2 d.p.

The centre of mass has coordinates (5.53, 3.33).

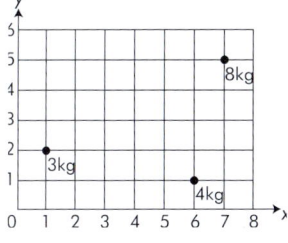

Mechanics — Centre of Mass

Centre of mass of a uniform lamina
AQA: M2; EDEXCEL: M2; OCR: M2; WJEC: M1; NICCEA: M3

A lamina is a very thin, flat sheet.

To find the centre of mass of a uniform lamina, follow these steps.

Step 1: Divide the lamina into regular geometric parts (i.e. squares, rectangles or triangles).

Step 2: Find the area of each part. This represents its mass.

Step 3: Find the geometric centre of each part.

Step 4: Find the centre of mass using your answers from steps 2 and 3.

Freely suspended lamina
AQA: M2; EDEXCEL: M2; OCR: M2; WJEC: M1; NICCEA: M3

When a lamina is freely suspended from one of its vertices, then its centre of mass lies directly below the point of suspension.

Example

a Find the centre of mass of the uniform plane lamina ABCD.

b If the lamina is suspended from point A, find the angle that side AD makes with the vertical.

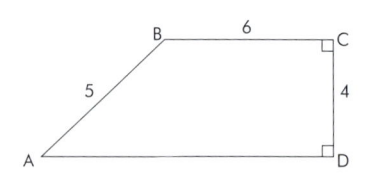

Solution

a Step 1: Divide the lamina into parts X and Y as shown.

Step 2: Triangle X has area 6 square units. Rectangle Y has area 24 square units.

Step 3: The centre of triangle X is $(2, \frac{4}{3})$ and of rectangle Y is $(6, 2)$.

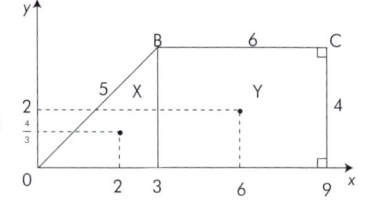

MECHANICS — CENTRE OF MASS

Step 4: The centre of mass is given by:

$M = 6 + 24 = 30$

$\bar{x} = \frac{1}{30} \sum_{i=1}^{2} m_i x_i = \frac{1}{30}(6 \times 2 + 24 \times 6) = 5.2$

$\bar{y} = \frac{1}{30} \sum_{i=1}^{2} m_i y_i = \frac{1}{30}(6 \times \frac{4}{3} + 24 \times 2) = 1.9$

The centre of mass of the lamina has coordinates (5.2, 1.9).

b When the lamina is suspended from A it will hang so that the centre of mass is directly below A as shown in the diagram.

You need to find the angle marked θ.

Using trigonometry gives:

$\tan \theta = \frac{1.9}{5.2}$

$\theta = 20°$ to 1 d.p.

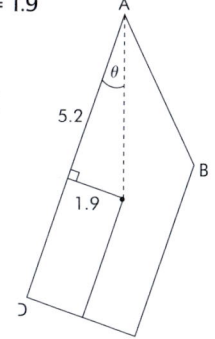

Centre of mass for composite bodies
AQA: M1; EDEXCEL: M3; OCR: M2; WJEC: M1; NICCEA: M3

You can find the centre of mass for composite bodies by considering each component separately. For each component, find a particle representing the centre of mass and express its position in terms of unit vectors **i** and **j**. Then, using the mass of each component, you can find the centre of mass of the composite body.

Example

Find the centre of mass for the composite body shown, given that the base has mass of 8 kg and the remaining bars are 1.2 m long and have a mass of 3 kg.

Solution

The table overleaf gives the mass of each component and the position of its centre of mass.

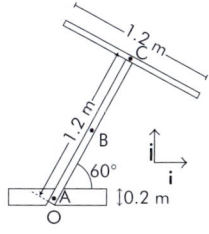

51

MECHANICS   CENTRE OF MASS

Particle	Mass(kg)	Position
A	8	$0.1\mathbf{j}$
B	3	$0.6\cos 60°\mathbf{i} + 0.6\sin 60°\mathbf{j}$
C	3	$1.2\cos 60°\mathbf{i} + 1.2\sin 60°\mathbf{j}$

Note: Each particle represents the centre of mass of each individual component relative to O.

So the centre of mass, $\bar{\mathbf{r}}$, is given by:

$$\bar{\mathbf{r}} = \frac{8 \times 0.1\mathbf{j} + 3 \times (0.3\mathbf{i} + 0.3\sqrt{3}\mathbf{j}) + 3 \times (0.6\mathbf{i} + 0.6\sqrt{3}\mathbf{j})}{8 + 3 + 3}$$

$$= \frac{2.7\mathbf{i} + 5.48\mathbf{j}}{14} = 0.19\mathbf{i} + 0.39\mathbf{j}$$

Centre of mass by integration
AQA: M2; EDEXCEL: M2; NICCEA: M3

Centre of mass of a uniform lamina

The centre of mass of a uniform lamina is given by:

$$\bar{x} = \frac{\int_a^b yx\,dx}{\int_a^b y\,dx} \text{ and } \bar{y} = \frac{\int_a^b \frac{1}{2}y^2\,dx}{\int_a^b y\,dx}$$

Centre of mass of a uniform solid of revolution

The centre of mass of a uniform solid of revolution is given by:

$$\bar{x} = \frac{\int_a^b y^2 x\,dx}{\int_a^b y^2\,dx}$$

Example

A lamina is bounded by the curve $y = 2\sqrt{x}$, the x-axis and the line $x = 1$. Find the coordinates of the centre of mass.

MECHANICS — CENTRE OF MASS

Solution

$$\bar{x} = \frac{\int_0^1 2x^{\frac{3}{2}}dx}{\int_0^1 2\sqrt{x}\,dx} = \frac{\left[\frac{2}{5}x^{\frac{5}{2}}\right]_0^1}{\left[\frac{2}{3}x^{\frac{3}{2}}\right]_0^1} = \frac{2/5}{2/3} = \frac{3}{5} = 0.6$$

$$\bar{y} = \frac{\int_0^1 2x\,dx}{\int_0^1 2\sqrt{x}\,dx} = \frac{\left[\frac{x^2}{2}\right]_0^1}{\left[\frac{2}{3}x^{\frac{3}{2}}\right]_0^1} = \frac{1/2}{2/3} = \frac{3}{4} = 0.75$$

The coordinates of the centre of mass are (0.6, 0.75).

Example

A frustum is formed by slicing a cone of height h at the point $\frac{h}{3}$ from the vertex, as shown.

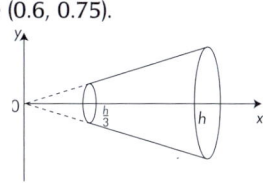

Find the distance of the centre of mass of the frustum from its base.

Solution

Let the equation of line passing through the origin be $y = kx$.

$$\therefore \bar{x} = \frac{\int_{\frac{h}{3}}^{h} k^2 x^2}{\int_{\frac{h}{3}}^{h} k^2 x^2 dx} = \frac{\left[\frac{x^4}{4}\right]_{\frac{h}{3}}^{h}}{\left[\frac{x^3}{3}\right]_{\frac{h}{3}}^{h}} = \frac{\frac{h^4}{4} - \frac{h^4}{324}}{\frac{h^3}{3} - \frac{h^3}{81}} = h \frac{\left(\frac{1}{4} - \frac{1}{324}\right)}{\left(\frac{1}{3} - \frac{1}{81}\right)} = \frac{10h}{13}$$

The height of the centre of mass from the base of the frustum
$= h - \frac{10h}{13} = \frac{3h}{13}$.

53

Mechanics — Circular motion

Circular paths

AQA: M2, M3; EDEXCEL: M3; OCR: M2; WJEC: M3; NICCEA: M2

Consider an object P that moves with constant speed around a circular path with centre O and radius r.

The angular speed ω of the point P about the fixed point O is defined as the rate of change of θ with time.

$\omega = \frac{d\theta}{dt}$ rad s^{-1} and integrating this gives $\theta = \omega t$.

The **position vector** of P is given by:

$\mathbf{r} = r\cos(\omega t)\mathbf{i} + r\sin(\omega t)\mathbf{j}$

While the speed of the particle may be constant, its velocity changes, as it is a vector with varying direction.

The **tangential velocity** v of P is given by:

$v = r\omega$

The **velocity vector** of P is given by the derivative of the position vector with respect to time

$\mathbf{v} = -r\omega\sin(\omega t)\mathbf{i} + r\omega\cos(\omega t)\mathbf{j}$

As the velocity of the particle is changing so the particle must be accelerating.

The acceleration is always directed towards the centre of the circle. It is known as **radial acceleration**, and its magnitude is given by:

$a = r\omega^2 = \frac{v^2}{r}$ (note: $\omega = \frac{v}{r}$)

The **acceleration vector** of P is given by the derivative of the velocity vector with respect to time.

$a = -r\omega^2\cos(\omega t)\mathbf{i} - r\omega^2\sin(\omega t)\mathbf{j}$
$ = -\omega^2(r\cos(\omega t)\mathbf{i} + r\sin(\omega t)\mathbf{j})$
$ = -\omega^2\mathbf{r}$

Thus the acceleration vector is related to the position vector. The negative sign indicates it is directed towards the centre.

MECHANICS — CIRCULAR MOTION

Circular motion and force
AQA: M3; EDEXCEL: M3; OCR: M2; WJEC: M3; NICCEA: M2

The radial acceleration of a particle acted upon by a force **F** is known as the centripetal force toward the centre of the circle. Its magnitude is given by:

$F = ma = \frac{mv^2}{r}$ or $F = mr\omega^2$

The conical pendulum
AQA: M3; EDEXCEL: M3; OCR: M2; WJEC: M3; NICCEA: M2

A common application involving circular motion is the conical pendulum.

The motion of a conical pendulum can be summarised as follows.

A particle P of mass m describes a horizontal circle centre O and radius r while attached to a string of length l. The distance of P vertically below A is h, as shown in the diagram.

Forces acting on P are:
- its weight $= mg$
- tension in the string T
- a resultant centripetal force towards the centre O equal to $mr\omega^2$

Resolving forces vertically:

$T\cos\theta = mg$ (1)

Using $F = ma$ horizontally:

$T\sin\theta = mr\omega^2$
$\quad\quad\quad = ml\sin\theta \times \omega^2$ (2)
$T = ml\omega^2$ (3)

Other important results include:

- $\frac{(2)}{(1)}$: $\frac{T\sin\theta}{T\cos\theta} = \frac{mr\omega^2}{mg}$ i.e. $\tan\theta = \frac{r\omega^2}{g}$

- $\tan\theta = \frac{r\omega^2}{g}$ and $\tan\theta = \frac{r}{h}$

  $\therefore \frac{r}{h} = \frac{r\omega^2}{g}$ i.e. $h = \frac{g}{\omega^2}$

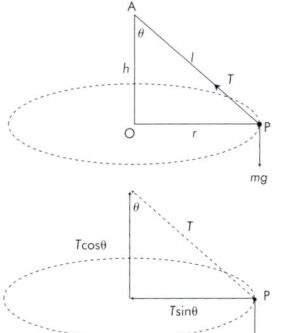

MECHANICS — CIRCULAR MOTION

- also $\omega = \frac{v}{r}$, substituting into $h = \frac{g}{\omega^2}$ gives:

$$h = \frac{gr^2}{v^2} \Rightarrow v^2 = \frac{gr^2}{h} \text{ i.e. } v = r\left(\frac{g}{h}\right)^{\frac{1}{2}}$$

- substituting (**3**) into (**1**) gives:

$$ml\omega^2 \cos\theta = mg \Rightarrow \cos\theta = \frac{g}{l\omega^2}$$

Example

Two particles of masses $2m$ kg and $3m$ kg are attached to either end of a light, inextensible string of length $7l$ metres, which passes through a small, vertical, frictionless ring R. The heavier particle, A, hangs vertically at a distance of $4l$ below the ring while the other particle, B, describes a horizontal circle, centre O. Find:

a the distance OR and the radius of the horizontal circle, OB

b the angular velocity of B about O.

Solution

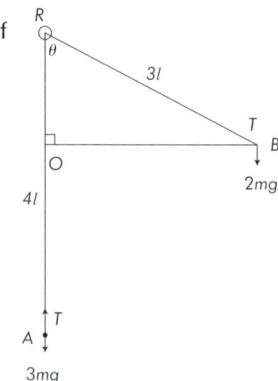

Since two particles are involved you need to assess the forces at each end of the string. As the ring is frictionless, the tensions in AR and BR are equal.

Resolving forces at B gives:

- vertically: $T\cos\theta = 2mg$ (**1**)
- horizontally:

$$T\sin\theta = 2mr\omega^2$$
$$= 2m \times 3l\sin\theta \times \omega^2$$
$$T = 6ml\omega^2 \quad (\mathbf{2})$$

Resolving forces at A gives:

$$T = 3mg \quad (\mathbf{3})$$

a From (3): $T = 3mg$ substituting into (1) gives:

$$3mg\cos\theta = 2mg$$
$$\cos\theta = \tfrac{2}{3}$$

So $\dfrac{OR}{3l} = \dfrac{2}{3} \Rightarrow OR = 2l$ metres

Radius OB is given by:

$$(3l)^2 - (2l)^2 = (OB)^2$$
$$9l^2 - 4l^2 = (OB)^2$$
$$5l^2 = (OB)^2$$
$$OB = \sqrt{5}\,l$$

b From (2): $T = 6ml\omega^2$

$$\frac{g}{2l} = \omega^2$$

$$\omega = \sqrt{\frac{g}{2l}} \text{ rad s}^{-1}$$

Banked tracks

AQA: M3; EDEXCEL: M3; OCR: M2; WJEC: M3; NICCEA: M2

Banked tracks are intended to reduce the tendency for a vehicle to slide outwards as it travels around a circular path at high speeds. This is achieved as the reaction force of the road surface on the car increases the maximum centripetal force.

The forces acting at O are:

- the weight of the vehicle $= mg$
- a resultant centripetal force inwards towards the centre $O = \dfrac{mv^2}{r}$
- the sideways friction (thrust) $= F$
  (**Note:** F always acts along the slope as shown.)
- The normal reaction, R, at right angles to the slope.

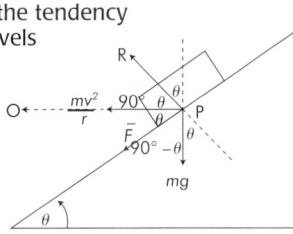

Note: Although the forces act on the centre of mass of the vehicle, it is often easier to resolve forces at point P as shown. The forces on the vehicle are vectors and they can be resolved at any point, provided their magnitude and direction are unchanged.

Resolving the forces at P:

1 down the slope: $\frac{mv^2}{r}\cos\theta = F + mg\sin\theta$ (1)

2 At right angles to the slope: $\frac{mv^2}{r}\sin\theta = R - mg\cos\theta$ (2)

Thus from (1):
$$F = mg\left(\frac{v^2\cos\theta}{gr} - \sin\theta\right) = mg\cos\theta\left(\frac{v^2}{gr} - \tan\theta\right)$$
and from (2):
$$R = mg\left(\frac{v^2\sin\theta}{gr} + \cos\theta\right) = mg\cos\theta\left(\frac{v^2}{gr}\tan\theta + 1\right)$$

Important features

a Since $0 \leq \theta \leq \frac{\pi}{2}$, $R > 0$ i.e. the normal reaction of the road on the vehicle is always present.

b When $F = 0$, there is no sideways friction between the wheels and the road.

Forces at P may also be resolved horizontally and vertically depending on the question.

3 Resolving forces horizontally at P:
$\frac{mv^2}{r} = R\sin\theta + F\cos\theta$ (3)

4 Resolving forces vertically at P:
$R\cos\theta - F\sin\theta = mg$ (4)

Equations (3) and (4) may be solved simultaneously to obtain equations (1) and (2).

Example

A car is travelling around a circular track which is banked at an angle of 10°. If the radius of the track is 250 metres, find the maximum safe velocity of the car, so that it does not slip.

Solution

Let the mass of the car be m. Since there is no tendency to slip, the frictional force $F = 0$.

Resolving forces horizontally:

$R \sin 10° = \dfrac{mv^2}{250}$ (1)

Resolving forces vertically:

$R \cos 10° = mg$ (2)

$\dfrac{(1)}{(2)}$: $\tan 10° = \dfrac{v^2}{250g}$

i.e. $v = \sqrt{250 g \tan 10°} = 20.8 \text{ m s}^{-1}$ to 1 d.p.

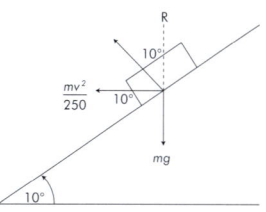

Motion in a vertical circle

AQA: M3; EDEXCEL: M3; OCR: M3; WJEC: M3; NICCEA: M4

In questions on vertical circular motion, you will often need to:

- find the speed of the particle, using conservation of energy
- consider the radial forces necessary to maintain circular motion.

Example

A particle, P, of mass 2 kg is attached to the end of a light string of length 0.6 m. The other end of the string is fixed at O. The particle is projected at 4 m s^{-1} from the horizontal. Find the speed and tension in the string at the point when OP is horizontal.

Solution

The kinetic energy lost = $\dfrac{1}{2} \times 2 \times 4^2 - \dfrac{1}{2} \times 2 \times v^2 = 16 - v^2$

As this will be equal to the potential energy gained:

$16 - v^2 = mgh = 2 \times 9.8 \times 0.6 = 11.76$

∴ $v^2 = 4.24$

$v = 2.06 \text{ m s}^{-1}$

Horizontally: $T = \dfrac{mv^2}{r} = \dfrac{2 \times 4.24}{0.6} = 14.1$ N to 1 d.p.

Hooke's law
AQA: M3; EDEXCEL: M3; OCR: M3; WJEC: M1; NICCEA: M4

When a spring is stretched it exerts a tension force, the magnitude of which is given by **Hooke's law**:

$T = ke$, where: k is the **spring's stiffness** and
e is the **extension** of the spring.

For springs of different lengths, the spring's stiffness is given by:

$k = \frac{\lambda}{l}$, where: λ is the **modulus of elasticity** and
l is the **natural length** of the spring.

A compressed spring exerts a thrust force of ke, where e is the distance it is **compressed**.

Hooke's law applies in the same way to elastic strings that are under tension, but the difference is that a string cannot exert a thrust force.

Work done by a variable force
AQA: M3; EDEXCEL: M2, M3; OCR: M2; WJEC: M2; NICCEA: M3

The work done by a variable force in moving from $x = a$ to $x = b$ is given by:

$$\int_a^b F\,dx = \tfrac{1}{2}mv^2 - \tfrac{1}{2}mu^2$$

where u is the speed when $x = a$ and v is the speed when $x = b$.

Elastic potential energy
AQA: M2; EDEXCEL: M3; OCR: M3; WJEC: M2; NICCEA: M3

The elastic potential energy (EPE) of a spring is its capacity for doing work as it returns to its natural length. It is given by:

Work done = EPE = $\int_0^e kx\,dx = \left[\tfrac{1}{2}kx^2\right]_0^e = \tfrac{1}{2}ke^2$

As $T = \frac{\lambda x}{l}$, the elastic potential energy can also be expressed as:

EPE = $\frac{\lambda e^2}{2l}$

Example

A spring of natural length, 20 cm and modulus of elasticity 20 N is compressed by 10 cm and used to project a particle P of mass 0.4 kg. Find the speed of P when it loses contact with the spring assuming all the energy is transferred to P.

Solution

$EPE = \frac{\lambda e^2}{2l} = \frac{20 \times (0.1)^2}{2 \times 0.2} = 0.5$ J

Now all the EPE is converted to kinetic energy, so:

$KE = \frac{1}{2}mv^2 = \frac{1}{2} \times 0.4 \times v^2 = 0.2v^2$

This gives: $0.2v^2 = 0.5 \Rightarrow v = 1.6$ m s^{-1} to 1 d.p.

MECHANICS — SIMPLE HARMONIC MOTION

Defining simple harmonic motion
AQA: M2; EDEXCEL: M3; OCR: M3; WJEC: M3; NICCEA: M3

There are many aspects of this motion that you need to know. If you have a thorough understanding of these, you should achieve a very high level in these questions.

- The basic equations of motion are $x = a\cos(\omega t + \alpha)$ or $x = a\sin(\omega t + \alpha)$. From this, the values of a (the amplitude), ω and α may be obtained.
- In the standard case where $\alpha = 0$, the initial position of the particle is $x = a$. Then the particle commences its motion at one of the extremities. The motion of the particle is as follows.

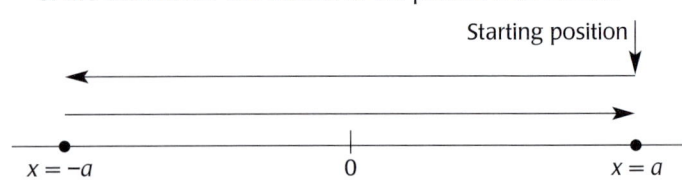

Starting position

$x = -a$ 0 $x = a$

Description of the motion

The particle commences its motion at $x = a$ and moves towards and past the centre O to $x = -a$. At $x = -a$ it stops, reverses direction and moves towards and past the centre to $x = a$ again. The motion continues in this fashion.

- The particle is moving in SHM provided $\ddot{x} = -\omega^2 x$ where ω is a constant and $\ddot{x}$ is the second derivative of x.
- The period, T, of the motion is given by:

$T = \dfrac{2\pi}{\omega}$ seconds

The period of oscillation of a mass in a spring system is:

$2\pi\sqrt{\dfrac{m}{k}}$ or $2\pi\sqrt{\dfrac{ml}{\lambda}}$

where $k = \dfrac{\lambda}{l}$

MECHANICS — SIMPLE HARMONIC MOTION

Note: The acceleration for a mass-spring system is given by:

$\ddot{x} = -\frac{kx}{m}$

$= -\frac{\lambda x}{ml}$, where $k = \frac{\lambda}{l}$

This differential equation has solutions of the form $x = a\cos(\omega t + \alpha)$.

$\therefore \omega = \sqrt{\frac{\lambda}{ml}}$ or $\omega = \sqrt{\frac{k}{m}}$

- The formula $v^2 = \omega^2(a^2 - x^2)$ or $v = \omega\sqrt{a^2 - x^2}$ is very important and you should memorise it. It is the easiest and most efficient method to find v, given x.

- From the formula $\ddot{x} = -\omega^2 x$, you can see that:
  - → the acceleration is zero at the centre i.e. $x = 0$
  - → the acceleration is a maximum (or minimum) at the end-points i.e. $x = a$ (or $x = -a$) and has magnitude $\omega^2 a$.

- The maximum speed is ωa which occurs at the centre O (when $x = 0$).

- The amplitude, a, is the distance from the centre to either of the end-points.

Example

A particle moves so that its distance x cm from a fixed point O at time t seconds is $x = 2\cos 3t$.

a Show that the particle is moving in simple harmonic motion.

b What is the amplitude and period of motion?

c What is the speed of the particle when the particle is 1 cm to the right of O?

Solution

a $x = 2\cos 3t \Rightarrow \dot{x} = -6\sin 3t \Rightarrow \ddot{x} = -18\cos 3t$

Now, $\ddot{x} = -18\cos 3t = -9(2\cos 3t) = -9x$

Since $\ddot{x}$ is in the form $\ddot{x} = -\omega^2 x$, the motion is simple harmonic.

b $\ddot{x} = -9x$

$\therefore \omega^2 = 9 \Rightarrow \omega = 3$

Hence, the period $= T = \frac{2\pi}{\omega} = \frac{2\pi}{3}$ seconds

Amplitude a is given from $x = a\cos(\omega t + \alpha)$ i.e. $a = 2$ cm.

c $x = 1$, $v = \omega\sqrt{a^2 - x^2}$

At $x = 1$, speed $= \omega\sqrt{a^2 - x^2}$

$= 3\sqrt{2^2 - 1^2} = 3\sqrt{3}$ cm s^{-1}

The simple pendulum
AQA: M2; EDEXCEL: M3; OCR: M3; WJEC: M3; NICCEA: M3

A simple pendulum can be considered to be a point mass suspended from a string. The motion of a simple pendulum is SHM in that the equation for the angular displacement is:

$$\ddot{\theta} = -\frac{g}{l}\theta$$

For small amplitudes, the period of such a pendulum can be approximated by:

$$T = 2\pi\sqrt{\frac{l}{g}}$$

STATISTICS — THE POISSON DISTRIBUTION

The Poisson distribution

AQA: S4; EDEXCEL: S2; OCR: S2, S3; WJEC: S2, MS; NICCEA: S1

The Poisson distribution is used to model the number of occurrences of a particular event in a prescribed time or space interval. It is given by:

$P_\lambda(x) = \frac{\lambda^x e^{-\lambda}}{x!}$, $x = 0, 1, 2, \ldots$

mean $= \mu = \lambda$ and variance $= \sigma^2 = \lambda$

where λ is the mean number of occurrences per unit time or space.

Poisson variables are **additive**.

i.e. if $X \sim \text{Poi}(\mu_x)$ and $Y \sim \text{Poi}(\mu_y)$

then: $X + Y \sim \text{Poi}(\mu_x + \mu_y)$

Example

The number of false alarms in a suburb of London averages 1.8 per day. Assuming a Poisson distribution is appropriate, find the probability that at least two false alarms will occur on a given day.

Solution

$$P_{1.8}(X \geq 2) = 1 - (P_{1.8}(X = 0) + P_{1.8}(X = 1))$$
$$= 1 - (e^{-1.8} + 1.8e^{-1.8})$$
$$= 0.537 \text{ to 3 d.p.}$$

STATISTICS — CONTINUOUS RANDOM VARIABLES

Probability density function
AQA: S4; EDEXCEL: S2; OCR: S2, S3; WJEC: S2, MS; NICCEA: S1

A probability density function is a non-negative function defined on a continuous interval so that the area under the curve is equal to 1.

If f(x) is valid for $a < x < b$, then $\int_a^b f(x)\,dx = 1$.

The mean and variance are given by:

Mean: $E(X) = \mu = \int_{\text{all } x} x f(x)\,dx$

Variance: $\text{Var}(X) = \sigma^2 = E(X^2) - \mu^2 = \int_{\text{all } x} x^2 f(x)\,dx - \mu^2$

The cumulative distribution function
AQA: S2; OCR: S2, S3; WJEC: S2

A cumulative distribution function describes the integral of the probability density function: a random variable X has the cumulative distribution function F(x), if the probability of an experiment to yield an $X < x_1$ is given by:

$F(x_1) = P(X < x_1) = \int_a^{x_1} f(x)\,dx$ for $a \leq x_1 \leq b$

Note: This also means that $f(x) = \frac{d}{dx} F(x)$

Example

$f(x) = kx^2$ for $0 \leq x \leq 1$. Find k and the median m.

Solution

$\int_0^1 kx^2\,dx = 1 \Rightarrow k\left[\frac{x^3}{3}\right]_0^1 = 1 \Rightarrow k = 3$

The median, m, is the value 50% of the way through the distribution i.e. $F(m) = 0.5$.

$F(m) = \int_0^m 3x^2\,dx = [x^3]_0^m = m^3$

$\therefore m^3 = 0.5 \Rightarrow m = 0.79$ to 2 d.p.

STATISTICS — **CONTINUOUS RANDOM VARIABLES**

Rectangular distribution

AQA: S4; OCR: S2; WJEC: S2, MS

Consider a random variable that is rectangularly distributed on $a \leq x \leq b$.

The area of the rectangle must be 1, hence:

$f(x) = \dfrac{1}{b-a}$

$E(X) = \dfrac{1}{2}(a+b)$ and

$\text{Var}(X) = \dfrac{1}{12}(b-a)^2$

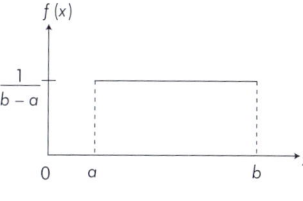

Linear combinations of random variables

AQA: S3; OCR: S3; WJEC: S2, MS; NICCEA: S2

You need to be familiar with the following results concerning **expectation algebra**.

Variable	Expected value	Variance
aX	$E(aX) = aE(X)$	$\text{Var}(aX) = a^2\text{Var}(X)$
$aX + b$	$E(aX + b) = aE(X) + b$	$\text{Var}(aX + b) = a^2\text{Var}(X)$
$aX + bY$	$E(aX + bY)$ $= aE(X) + bE(Y)$	$\text{Var}(aX + bY) =$ $a^2\text{Var}(X) + b^2\text{Var}(Y)$
$aX - bY$	$E(aX - bY)$ $= aE(X) - bE(Y)$	$\text{Var}(aX - bY) =$ $a^2\text{Var}(X) + b^2\text{Var}(Y)$

An important result concerning normal distributions states:

If X and Y are normally distributed, such that $X \sim N(\mu_1, \sigma_1^2)$, $Y \sim N(\mu_2, \sigma_2^2)$ then the following are also normally distributed:

Sum: $\qquad X + Y \sim N(\mu_1 + \mu_2, \sigma_1^2 + \sigma_2^2)$

Difference: $\qquad X - Y \sim N(\mu_1 - \mu_2, \sigma_1^2 - \sigma_2^2)$

Multiple: $\qquad aX \sim N(a\mu_1, a^2\sigma_1^2)$

Poisson approximation to binomial

AQA: S2; EDEXCEL: S2; OCR: S2; WJEC: S1

When p, the probability of failure on a given trial is small ($p \leq 0.1$) and n, the number of trials is large ($n \geq 30$), the binomial distribution can be approximated by the **Poisson distribution** with a **mean of np** i.e. Poi(np).

Example

A factory produces batteries, of which 5% are defective. If a sample of 40 batteries are chosen, find the probability that fewer than 5 are defective.

Solution

p = probability of failure = 0.05, $n = 40$, $np = 2$

As n is large and p is small, use the Poisson approximation, $X \sim$ Poi(2).

$P(X < 5) = P(X = 0) + P(X = 1) + P(X = 2) + P(X = 3) + P(X = 4)$

$= e^{-2} + 2e^{-2} + \frac{2^2 e^{-2}}{2!} + \frac{2^3 e^{-2}}{3!} + \frac{2^4 e^{-2}}{4!}$

$= e^{-2} + 2e^{-2} + 2e^{-2} + \frac{4}{3}e^{-2} + \frac{2}{3}e^{-2} = 7e^{-2}$

$= 0.947$ to 3 d.p.

Normal approximation to binomial

AQA: S2; EDEXCEL: S2; OCR: S2; WJEC: S2, MS; NICCEA: S3

When p and n are such that $np > 5$ and $nq > 5$, where $q = 1 - p$, the binomial distribution can be approximated by the normal distribution with a mean of np and variance of npq.

i.e. $X \sim N(np, npq)$

Since the normal distribution is continuous, whereas the binomial is discrete, use a correction called the **continuity correction**.

To include the outcome $X = 9$, you must include the entire interval from 8.5 to 9.5. So $P(X \leq 9)$ is calculated as $P(X < 9.5)$. On the other hand, $P(X < 9)$ excludes the outcome $X = 9$, so exclude the entire interval 8.5–9.5 and calculate $P(X < 8.5)$ from the normal table.

STATISTICS — APPROXIMATING DISTRIBUTIONS

Example

The probability that someone drinks tea daily is 0.3. If 40 people are chosen randomly, find the probability that at least 10 drink tea daily.

Solution

$p = 0.3$, $q = 0.7$, $np = 12 > 5$, $nq = 28 > 5$

Since np and nq are both larger than 5, use the normal approximation, $X \sim N(np, npq)$ i.e. $X \sim N(12, 8.4)$. Applying the continuity correction, $P(X \geq 10)$ becomes $P(X > 9.5)$.

$$P(X > 9.5) = P\left(Z > \frac{9.5 - 12}{\sqrt{8.4}}\right) = P(Z > -0.863)$$

$$= \Phi(0.863) = 0.8059 \text{ to 4 d.p.}$$

Normal approximation to Poisson
AQA: S2; EDEXCEL: S2; OCR: S2; WJEC: S2, MS; NICCEA: S3

For large λ ($\lambda > 15$), the Poisson distribution can be approximated by the normal distribution with mean λ and variance λ ($X \sim N(\lambda, \lambda)$). Since the Poisson distribution is discrete, use a continuity correction.

Example

If $X \sim \text{Poi}(30)$, find $P(24 < X < 46)$.

Solution

Since λ is large, $X \sim N(30, 30)$ approximately.

Applying the continuity correction, $P(24 < X < 46)$ becomes $P(24.5 < X < 45.5)$.

$$P(24.5 < X < 45.5) = P\left(\frac{24.5 - 30}{\sqrt{30}} < Z < \frac{45.5 - 30}{\sqrt{30}}\right)$$

$$= P(-1.004 < Z < 2.830)$$
$$= P(Z < 2.83) - P(Z < -1.004)$$
$$= 0.9977 - (1 - P(Z > 1.004))$$
$$= 0.9977 - (1 - 0.8422)$$
$$= 0.8399 \text{ to 4 d.p.}$$

STATISTICS — SAMPLES AND ESTIMATION

Sampling
AQA: S2; EDEXCEL: S2, S3; OCR: S2; WJEC: S1, MS; NICCEA: S2, S3

The purpose of a sample is to provide an estimate for a particular population characteristic when it is not possible to assess the entire population.

You should be familiar with the following sampling techniques:

- **convenience sampling** – choose the first person who comes along
- **random sampling** – choose a sample in which all items are equally likely to be chosen
- **systematic sampling** – involves random sampling, whereby you use some system to select the items of the population to be sampled
- **stratified sampling** – choose a sample that is representative of the population being considered; for example, if the population to be surveyed has twice as many men as women then the sample should also contain twice as many men than women
- **quota sampling** – involves choosing a sample with specific characteristics beforehand (e.g. blue collar workers, children over 12 etc.).

Unbiased estimates
AQA: S4; EDEXCEL: S3; OCR: S2; WJEC: S3; NICCEA: S2

A number that describes a population is called a **parameter**. A number that can be computed from the data is called a **statistic**.

The purpose of sampling or experimentation is usually to use statistics to make estimates about unknown parameters.

A statistic used to estimate a parameter is an **unbiased estimate** of the parameter if its expectation is equal to the true value of the parameter. i.e.

E(estimate) = true value of the parameter

STATISTICS — SAMPLES AND ESTIMATION

Unbiased estimates for the mean, proportion and variance are:

Mean μ: $\mu = \bar{x} = \frac{\sum x}{n}$ $\bar{x}$ is the sample mean

Proportion p: $\hat{p} = p_s$ p_s is the sample proportion

Variance σ^2: $\hat{\sigma}^2 = \frac{n}{n-1}\sigma^2$ σ^2 is the sample variance

In exams you may sometimes be given only summary data such as $\sum x$ or $\sum x^2$, in which case you may need the following alternative formulae for the variance:

$$\hat{\sigma}^2 = \sum \frac{(x-\bar{x})^2}{n-1} \text{ or } \hat{\sigma}^2 = \frac{1}{n-1}\left(\sum x^2 - \frac{(\sum x)^2}{n}\right)$$

On a calculator the value of $\hat{\sigma}$ is given by the $\boxed{\sigma_{x_{n-1}}}$ key.

Sampling distributions

AQA: S4, S5; EDEXCEL: S3; OCR: S2; WJEC: S2, S3; NICCEA: S2

Consider all possible samples of size n that can be drawn from a given population. For each sample, you can calculate a statistic (e.g. mean, proportion) that will vary from sample to sample. Thus, you obtain a distribution of the statistic, called its **sampling distribution**.

Sampling distribution of the means

If all possible samples of size n are drawn from a finite population, the distribution of the sample means ($\bar{X}_n$) are summarised as follows.

- If the population is normally distributed i.e. $X \sim N(\mu, \sigma^2)$ then:
  $\bar{X}_n \sim N(\mu, \frac{\sigma^2}{n})$

- If the population is not normally distributed but n is sufficiently large ($n \geq 30$) then, by the central limit theorem:
  $\bar{X}_n \sim N(\mu, \frac{\sigma^2}{n})$ approximately.

The standard deviation of the distribution of means is known as the **standard error of the mean**. It is given by:

$$\text{standard error} = \sqrt{\frac{\sigma^2}{n}} = \frac{\sigma}{\sqrt{n}}$$

In general, the larger the sample size the smaller the standard error.

STATISTICS   SAMPLES AND ESTIMATION

Example

The results on a basic test required for a job at a bank in a big city are normally distributed with a mean of 68% and a standard deviation of 14%. A group of 40 applicants is chosen. Find the probability that the mean test score is greater than 72%.

Solution

If X is the test result at that bank, then $X \sim N(0.68, 0.14^2)$

For a group of 40, $\bar{X}_{40} \sim N\left(0.68, \dfrac{0.14^2}{40}\right)$

i.e. $\bar{X}_{40} \sim N(0.68, 0.00049)$

$$\begin{aligned} P(\bar{X}_{40} > 0.72) &= P\left(Z > \dfrac{0.72 - 0.68}{\sqrt{0.00049}}\right) \\ &= P(Z > 1.807) \\ &= 1 - 0.9646 \\ &= 0.035 \text{ to 3 d.p.} \end{aligned}$$

Sampling distribution of proportions

Consider a population where the proportion of success is p and proportion of failure is $q = 1 - p$.

If samples of size $n(n \geqslant 30)$ are drawn from this population, the sampling distribution of proportions

$p_s \sim N\left(p, \dfrac{pq}{n}\right)$

Note: From page 68, *Approximating distributions*, binomial probabilities may be approximated using the normal distribution. The mean and standard deviation of p_s are obtained by dividing the mean and standard deviation (np and $\sqrt{npq}$) of the binomial distribution by n.

The standard deviation of the distribution of proportions is known as the **standard error of proportion**. When using this distribution a continuity correction of $\pm \dfrac{1}{2n}$ is required.

Confidence intervals

AQA: S4, S5; EDEXCEL: S3; OCR: S3; WJEC: S3; NICCEA: S2, S3

A confidence interval is a range of values that has a specified probability of containing the parameter being estimated. The 90%, 95% and 99% confidence intervals are most commonly used.

Confidence intervals for means

The confidence limits for estimating the population mean, μ, are determined using the mean, $\bar{x}$, of a random sample of size n. They are given by:

$$\bar{x} \pm z_c \frac{\sigma}{\sqrt{n}}$$

Where z_c (which depends on the particular level of confidence desired) can be read from normal curve area tables.

For 90% confidence $z_c = 1.645$, for 95% confidence $z_c = 1.96$ and for 99% confidence $z_c = 2.576$.

Confidence intervals for proportions

The confidence limits for estimating the proportion of success p in a population, are determined using p_s, where p_s is the proportion of successes in the sample of size n. They are given by:

$$p_s \pm z_c \sqrt{\frac{p_s q_s}{n}}$$

where: $q_s = 1 - p_s$ and z_c can be read from the normal curve tables.

STATISTICS — HYPOTHESIS TESTING

An introduction to hypothesis testing

AQA: S4; EDEXCEL: S2; OCR: S2; WJEC: S2, S3; NICCEA: S2

In attempting to reach decisions, it is useful to make assumptions about the population involved. Such assumptions are called **hypotheses**. Procedures that enable you to determine whether to accept or reject hypotheses are called **tests of hypotheses** or **tests of significance**. There are two types of statistical hypothesis.

- **Null hypothesis**
  Denoted by H_0, is the particular assertion that is to be accepted or rejected. For example, if you want to decide whether a given coin is loaded, you might formulate the hypothesis that the coin is fair (i.e. $p = 0.5$, where p is the probability of heads).

- **Alternative hypothesis**
  Denoted by H_1, this specifies some alternative to H_0. The alternative hypothesis would be one of the following:
  - **one-tailed:** If H_1 says that the parameter is greater than the value specified for H_0, for example $H_1: p > 0.5$ or, a different alternative hypotheses could be $H_1: p < 0.5$.

  - **two-tailed:** If H_1 says that the parameter is not equal to the value specified for H_0, for example $H_1: p \neq 0.5$.

To decide whether H_0 is to be accepted or rejected, a **significance test** examines whether a sample taken from the population could have occurred by chance, given that H_0 is true.

The test statistic is determined from the sample. The test divides the set of possible values into the **acceptance region** and the **critical** (or **rejection**) **region**. The decision rule is based on the **significance level** of the test, which is the probability that the **test value** lies in the critical region if H_0 is true. The boundaries of the critical region are called the **critical values**. The significance level is given as a percentage. Often 10%, 5% or 1% is chosen.

Depending on the position of the test value, the decision is made. If the test value falls in the critical region, you reject H_0 in favour of H_1; otherwise, the conclusion is that there is insufficient evidence for rejecting H_0 and you say that that H_0 is not rejected.

STATISTICS — HYPOTHESIS TESTING

Type I and type II errors
AQA: S4, S5; OCR: S2

Type I error: Occurs if H_0 is rejected when it is, in fact, true.
P(type I error) = significance level

Type II error: Occurs if H_0 is accepted when it is, in fact, false.
P(type II error) = P(H_0 is accepted when H_1 is true)
The **power** of a test = 1 − P(type II error).

Critical values for z-tests
AQA: S4, S5; EDEXCEL: S3; OCR: S2; WJEC: S2; NICCEA: S2

The critical z-values for the most commonly used levels of significance are shown below; other values can be obtained from the normal curve area tables.

Level of significance	10%	5%	1%	0.5%
Critical values of z for one-tailed tests	−1.282 or 1.282	−1.645 or 1.645	−2.326 or 2.326	−2.576 or 2.576
Critical values of z for two-tailed tests	±1.645	±1.96	±2.576	±2.81

Z-test for the mean
AQA: S4, S5; EDEXCEL: S3; OCR: S2; WJEC: S2; NICCEA: S2

To test the hypothesis $H_0: \mu = \mu_0$ of a population with unknown μ and known standard deviation σ, find:

$$z = \frac{\bar{x} - \mu_0}{\sigma / \sqrt{n}}$$

In terms of a standard normal random variable Z, the probability value for a test of H_0 against:

$H_1: \mu > \mu_0$ is $P(Z \geq z)$ one-tailed (upper)

$H_1: \mu < \mu_0$ is $P(Z \leq z)$ one-tailed (lower)

$H_1: \mu \neq \mu_0$ is $2P(Z \geq |z|)$ two-tailed

STATISTICS — HYPOTHESIS TESTING

If the probability value is less than the significance level, then H_0 is rejected.

These probabilities are exact if the population is normal and approximately correct for large values of n in other cases.

Example

The weight of a certain type of cereal box is normally distributed with a mean mass of 368 g and a standard deviation of 15 g. A random sample of 25 boxes showed an average weight of 372.5 g. Is this sufficient evidence at the 5% level against the claim that the mean weight is 368 g?

Solution

$H_0: \mu = 368$; $H_1: \mu > 368$
$\bar{x} = 372.5$, so:
$$Z = \frac{\bar{x} - \mu}{\sigma/\sqrt{n}} = \frac{372.5 - 368}{15/\sqrt{25}} = 1.5$$
$P(z > 1.5) = 1 - 0.9332 = 0.0668$

Since $P(z > 1.5) > 0.05$, H_0 is not rejected.

There is not enough evidence, at the 5% level, that the mean mass of cereal boxes is greater than 368 g.

Z-test for the difference between means
EDEXCEL: S3; OCR: S3; WJEC: S3; NICCEA: S2, S3

If $\bar{X}_1$ and $\bar{X}_2$ are the sample means obtained in large samples of sizes n_1 and n_2 and standard deviation σ_1 and σ_2, then the null hypothesis that there is **no difference** between the population means (i.e. $\mu_1 = \mu_2$) can be tested as follows.

Test statistic $Z = \dfrac{\bar{X}_1 - \bar{X}_2 - (\mu_1 - \mu_2)}{\sqrt{\dfrac{\sigma_1^2}{n_1} + \dfrac{\sigma_2^2}{n_2}}} \sim N(0, 1)$

STATISTICS — HYPOTHESIS TESTING

Tests for a binomial proportion

EDEXCEL: S2; OCR: S2; WJEC: S3

Large sample size

When p and n are such that $np > 5$ and $nq > 5$, the binomial distribution can be approximated by a normal distribution with mean np and variance npq.

Test statistic $Z = \dfrac{X - np}{\sqrt{npq}} \sim N(0, 1)$, for large n

Note: Don't forget to apply a continuity correction – add 0.5 when testing in the lower tail and deduct 0.5 when testing in the upper tail.

To perform the hypothesis test follow these steps.

Step 1: Define the variable to be tested.

Step 2: State the null and alternative hypotheses and also the distribution if the null hypothesis is true.

Step 3: Verify that the normal approximation is appropriate by showing that $np > 5$ and $nq > 5$.

Step 4: Calculate the z-value, allowing for the continuity correction.

Step 5: Find the probability according to your alternative hypothesis. If the probability is less than the significance level reject H_0, otherwise do not reject H_0.

Step 6: Write a concluding statement that answers the question.

Example

A die is thrown 60 times and 14 sixes are obtained. Is this evidence, at the 5% level of significance, that the die is biased in favour of sixes?

Solution

Step 1: Let the probability of throwing a six be p.

Step 2: $H_0: p = \dfrac{1}{6}$, $H_1: p > \dfrac{1}{6}$ (die is biased)

If the null hypothesis is true, then $X \sim B(60, \frac{1}{6})$.

Step 3: $np = 60 \times \frac{1}{6} = 10 > 5$, $nq = 60 \times \frac{5}{6} = 50 > 5$
So $X \sim N(np, npq)$.

Step 4: The test value is $x = 14$; using the continuity correction you deduct 0.5 when testing for the upper tail i.e. use $x = 13.5$.
$$z = \frac{13.5 - np}{\sqrt{npq}} = \frac{13.5 - 10}{\sqrt{8.333}} = 1.212$$

Step 5: $P(Z \geq 1.212) = 1 - 0.8873 = 0.1127 > 0.05$ ∴ do not reject H_0.

Step 6: At the 5% level there is insufficient evidence to suggest that the die is biased in favour of sixes.

Small sample size

For small values of n, the normal approximation is not appropriate. Instead binomial probabilities are used to test the null hypothesis.

Example

A coin is tossed six times and comes up heads six times. Is this evidence at the 5% level of significance that the coin is biased in favour of heads?

Solution

Let the probability of heads be p.

H_0: $p = 0.5$, H_1: $p > 0.5$ (coin is biased in favour of heads)

If the null hypothesis is true, then $X \sim B(6, 0.5)$.

As n is small, the normal approximation is not appropriate and the binomial probabilities are used.

$P(X = 6) = \left(\frac{1}{2}\right)^6 = \frac{1}{64} = 0.01562 < 0.05$ ∴ reject H_0.

At the 5% level there is sufficient evidence to suggest that the coin is biased in favour of heads.

STATISTICS — HYPOTHESIS TESTING

Test for Poisson mean
EDEXCEL: S2; OCR: S2; WJEC: S2

When λ is **large**, the Poisson distribution can be approximated by a normal distribution with mean and variance λ i.e. $X \sim N(\lambda, \lambda)$. A continuity correction is needed.

When λ is **small**, poisson probabilities are used to determine whether the result is significant.

Example

The average number of accidents per month on a particular road is 6.2. In the month immediately following the introduction of a new speed camera, only two accidents occurred. Is this evidence at the 10% level of significance that speed cameras improve road safety?

Solution

Let X be the number of accidents in a given month, $X \sim \text{Poi}(\lambda)$.

$H_0: \lambda = 6.2$, $H_1: \lambda < 6.2$.

If the null hypothesis is true then, $X \sim \text{Poi}(6.2)$.

As λ is small, the normal approximation is not appropriate and the Poisson probabilities are used.

$P(X \leq 2) = e^{-6.2} + 6.2e^{-6.2} + \frac{6.2^2}{2!}e^{-6.2} = 0.0536 < 0.1$ $\therefore$ reject H_0.

At the 10% level there is sufficient evidence to suggest that speed cameras improve road safety.

The *t*-distribution
AQA: S4; OCR: S3; NICCEA: S3

Introduction

So far we have often used the fact that for large samples, the sampling distribution approximates a normal distribution, the approximation improving with increasing n. However, for small sample sizes ($n < 30$), this approximation is not good and grows worse with decreasing n.

STATISTICS — HYPOTHESIS TESTING

One important distribution that is used for small sample sizes to obtain confidence intervals for μ and perform significant tests is the **t-distribution**.

It has one parameter, v, known as the number of **degrees of freedom**. It is given by $v = (n - 1)$.

The relevant t-value is obtained from the t-distribution tables for a given value of v (denoted by $t(v)$). Tables give values of t for which $P(T < t) = p$, when p is the cumulative probability.

Confidence intervals

The confidence limits for estimating the population mean μ, are determined using the sample mean, $\bar{x}$, and the sample standard deviation, s, for a random sample of size n. They are given by:

$$\bar{x} \pm t^* \frac{s}{\sqrt{n}}$$

where t^* (which depends on the particular level of confidence desired) can be read from the t-distribution tables for $(n - 1)$ degrees of freedom.

Example

A random sample of five observations from $X \sim N(\mu, \sigma^2)$ were as follows.

21.50   23.78   55.95   68.24   52.73

Find a 90% confidence interval for μ.

Solution

Using a calculator gives:

$\bar{x} = 44.44$ and $s = 20.741$

The number of degrees of freedom, $v = (n - 1) = 4$.

From the τ-distribution table the 90% confidence value for t^* is 2.132.

The 90% confidence interval for μ is given by:

$$\bar{x} \pm t^* \frac{s}{\sqrt{n}} = 44.44 \pm 2.132 \left(\frac{20.741}{\sqrt{5}}\right)$$

$$= 44.44 \pm 19.78$$

$$= (24.66, 64.22) \text{ to 2 d.p.}$$

t-test for the mean

To test the hypothesis $H_0: \mu = \mu_0$ from a normal population with unknown variance, when the sample size is small, find:

$$t = \frac{\bar{x} - \mu_0}{s/\sqrt{n}} \quad \text{(Test statistic T)}$$

In terms of a random variable T having the $t(n-1)$ distribution, the probability value for a test of H_0 against:

$H_1: \mu > \mu_0$ is $P(T \geq t)$ one-tailed (upper)

$H_1: \mu < \mu_0$ is $P(T \leq t)$ one-tailed (lower)

$H_1: \mu \neq \mu_0$ is $2P(T \geq |t|)$ two-tailed

If the test statistic T is greater than the critical value, then H_0 is rejected.

Example

For the previous example, test at the 25% level the claim that μ is greater than 40.

Solution

$H_0: \mu = 40$; $H_1: \mu > 40$; $\bar{x} = 44.44$; $s = 20.741$, so

$$t = \frac{\bar{x} - \mu}{s/\sqrt{n}} = \frac{44.44 - 40}{20.741/\sqrt{5}} = 0.479 \text{ to 3 d.p.}$$

Using the *t*-table for $v = 4$, $P(T \geq t) = 0.75$ (one-tailed test, 25% in the upper tail), the critical value is 0.741.

As $t < 0.741$, there is not sufficient evidence to support the claim that μ is greater than 40.

t-test for the difference between means

Suppose that two random sample of size n_1 and n_2, with means $\bar{X}_1$ and $\bar{X}_2$ and standard deviations s_1 and s_2 respectively, are drawn from normal populations with equal standard deviations ($\sigma_1 = \sigma_2$). The null hypothesis that the samples come from the same population (i.e. $\mu_1 = \mu_2$ as well as $\sigma_1 = \sigma_2$) can be tested as follows.

Test statistic $T = \dfrac{\bar{X}_1 - \bar{X}_2 - (\mu_1 - \mu_2)}{\sigma\sqrt{\dfrac{1}{n_1} + \dfrac{1}{n_2}}}$

Where $\sigma^2 = \dfrac{n_1 s_1^2 + n_2 s_2^2}{n_1 + n_2 - 2}$ and

degrees of freedom, $v = (n_1 - 1) + (n_2 - 1) = n_1 + n_2 - 2$

Note: If you know σ^2, then you can use the *z*-test.

Test for correlation coefficient
EDEXCEL: S3; NICCEA: S2

From the AS course you may already be familiar with the product-moment correlation coefficient and **Spearman's rank correlation coefficient** for calculating the correlation between two variables. You can perform hypothesis testing to find the strength of the correlation. Follow these steps.

Step 1: Establish the null hypothesis. H_0: no correlation.

Step 2: Define the alternative hypothesis.
H_1: positive correlation – one-tailed (upper)
H_1: negative correlation – one-tailed (lower)
H_1: positive or negative correlation – two-tailed

Step 3: Find the critical values for the rejection region, based on the given significance level.

Step 4: Calculate the sample correlation coefficient and compare it with the critical value. If |sample value| > |critical value|, reject H_0; otherwise do not reject H_0.

Step 5: Write a concluding statement that answers the question.

STATISTICS — CHI-SQUARED DISTRIBUTION

Goodness of fit tests
EDEXCEL: S3; OCR: S3; NICCEA: S3

The chi-squared distribution (denoted by χ^2) is used to judge the appropriateness of a probability distribution to model a collection of observed frequencies. To perform a χ^2 goodness of fit test follow these steps.

Step 1: Establish the null and alternative hypotheses.
   H_0: model provides a good fit for these data
   H_1: model is not a good fit

Step 2: Calculate the **expected frequencies** (E) according to the probabilities suggested by the model.

   Note: It is generally agreed that *expected frequencies should not be less* than 5 as it may lead to erroneous conclusions. If it is, you will need to *amalgamate frequency cells* so that the expected frequency is no longer small.

Step 3: Denoting the *observed frequencies* by O, you can calculate the χ^2 statistic as follows.

   - Find the differences: $(O - E)$
   - Square the differences: $(O - E)^2$
   - Divide by the expected frequency: $\frac{(O - E)^2}{E}$
   - Find the χ^2 statistic, where $\chi^2 = \sum \frac{(O - E)^2}{E}$

Step 4: Find the number of degrees of freedom, v as follows.

   v = number of frequency cells − number of constraints

   Note: The **number of constraints** is usually 1 (as the expected and observed frequencies must be equivalent) but is increased by 1 for each population parameter which must be estimated from sample observations.

Step 5: Find (from χ^2 tables) the critical values for the rejection region based on v and the given significance level. It is often written as a subscript, hence χ^2_4 represents a chi-squared statistic with $v = 4$ (i.e. four degrees of freedom).

Statistics — Chi-squared distribution

Step 6: Compare the test statistic with the critical value:
If $\chi^2 >$ critical value, reject H_0 otherwise do not reject H_0.

Step 7: Write a concluding statement that answers the question.

Example

Amanda throws three dice 120 times and records the number of sixes she scores. The results are shown in the table.

Number of sixes	0	1	2	3
Frequency	64	45	10	1

Conduct an appropriate test at the 10% significance level, to test whether the binomial model, $B(3, \frac{1}{6})$ may be an appropriate fit for these data.

Solution

Step 1: H_0: the distribution fits $B(3, \frac{1}{6})$, H_1: the distribution doesn't fit.

Step 2: & Step 3:

Number of sixes	0	1	$\geqslant 2$
Observed, O	64	45	11
Expected, E	69.44	41.67	8.89
$\frac{(O-E)^2}{E}$	0.426	0.266	0.501

Note: Amalgamate outcomes 2 and 3 as the expected frequency must not be less than 5.

$\therefore \chi^2 = \sum \frac{(O-E)^2}{E} = 1.193$

Step 4: There are three categories so $v = 3 - 1 = 2$

Step 5: χ^2_2 at the 10% level is 4.605.

Step 6: Since $\chi^2 < 4.605$ do not reject H_0.

Step 7: We can conclude that the binomial model is a good fit for these data.

STATISTICS — CHI-SQUARED DISTRIBUTION

Contingency tables
AQA: S4; EDEXCEL: S3; OCR: S3; NICCEA: S3

You may also use the χ^2 test to test if two variables are independent or whether there is an association between them.

The data is often arranged in a two-way table known as a **contingency table**. Its size is described as 'the number of columns (c) by the number of rows (r)' it contains.

The null hypothesis, H_0, is that there is no association between the row and column variables. The alternative hypothesis, H_1, is that these variables are related.

The expected frequency for a particular cell (i, j) in a contingency table is given by:

$$\frac{(\text{sum of row } i) \times (\text{sum in column } j)}{\text{total number}}$$

For a contingency table with r rows and c columns the number of degrees of freedom is $(r-1)(c-1)$.

When there is only one degree of freedom the χ^2_1 statistic is best calculated using **Yates' continuity correction**:

$$\sum \frac{(|O - E| - 0.5)^2}{E}$$

DECISION AND DISCRETE MATHEMATICS — **GAME THEORY**

EDEXCEL: D2; OCR: D2

A two-person zero-sum game

A two-person **zero-sum game** is a game in which one player's winnings equal the other player's losses for every combination of strategies. The outcomes can be represented by the **pay-off matrix**. This matrix is a description of a zero-sum game. It shows that if player A adopts strategy a_1 and player B adopts strategy b_1 the the pay-offs for A and B are 2 and -2 respectively.

Pay-off matrix	Player B	
	b_1	b_2
Player A a_1	(2, −2)	(−4, 4)
a_2	(0, 0)	(1, −1)

Stable solutions

For a two-person, zero-sum game it is rational for each player to choose the strategy that will maximise their minimum pay-off (known as the **play-safe** strategy). The pair of strategies and pay-offs for which each player maximises his or her minimum pay-off is the 'solution to the game'. This represents the **stable solution** to the problem, referred to as the **saddle point**.

If the sum of the two values used to determine the play-safe strategies is **not zero**, then there is no saddle point and the game has **no stable solution**.

Mixed strategies

Repeated use of the same strategy is called a **pure strategy**. If a player in a game chooses from two or more strategies at random, according to specific probabilities, this choice is called a **mixed strategy**. It is used in the case where no stable solution exists.

If only two strategies exist for each player, the probabilities of each strategy can be found by solving a pair of equations. The expected long-term gain (or loss) for each player can then be calculated by substituting these probabilities back into either of the equations.

Where three or more strategies are possible, the optimal value can be computed using linear programming, one linear program for each player. The conditions are formulated as a linear programming problem which may then be solved by the simplex algorithm.

DECISION AND DISCRETE MATHEMATICS — GAME THEORY

Example

The table below shows a pay-off matrix for player 1 in a zero-sum game.

a Find the play-safe strategy for each player.

Pay-off matrix for Player 1		Player 2 C	D
Player A	A	1	−3
	B	−2	5

b Show that this game has no stable solution.

c Find the optimal strategy for each player.

d Find the expected longterm gain (or loss) for each player.

Solution

a The situation is shown in the pay-off matrices for players 1 and 2.

Pay-off matrix for Player 1		Player 2 C	D
Player 1	A	1	−3
	B	−2	5

Pay-off matrix for Player 2		Player 2 C	D
Player 1	A	−1	3
	B	2	−5

The play-safe strategy for player 1 is strategy B where the minimum pay-off is −2.

The play-safe strategy for player 2 is strategy C where the minimum pay-off is −1.

b Since $(-2) + (-1) \neq 0$, there is no saddle point and the game has no stable solution.

c To find the optimal strategy, proceed as follows.

Suppose player 1 chooses:

- strategy A with probability p and strategy B with probability $(1 - p)$

Now if player 2 chooses:

- strategy C, the expected gain for player 1 is given by:
  $p - 2(1 - p) = 3p - 2$
- strategy D, the expected gain for player 1is given by:
  $-3p + 5(1 - p) = 5 - 8p$

The optimal value occurs when these expressions are equal:

$3p - 2 = 5 - 8p$

$11p = 7$

$p = \frac{7}{11}$

∴ the optimal strategy for player 1 is to choose strategy A with probability $\frac{7}{11}$ and strategy B with probability $\frac{4}{11}$.

Suppose player 2 chooses:

- strategy C with probability q and strategy D with probability $(1 - q)$

Now if player 1 chooses:

- strategy A, the expected gain for player 2 is given by:
  $-q + 3(1 - q) = 3 - 4q$
- strategy B, the expected gain for player 2 is given by:
  $2q - 5(1 - q) = 7q - 5$

the optimal value occurs when these expressions are equal:

$3 - 4q = 7q - 5$

$8 = 11q$

$q = \frac{8}{11}$

∴ the optimal strategy for player 2 is to choose strategy C with probability $\frac{8}{11}$ and strategy D with probability $\frac{3}{11}$.

d The expected long-term gain for player 1 is given by:

$3 \times \frac{7}{11} - 2 = -\frac{1}{11}$

i.e. Player 1 will lose on average $-\frac{1}{11}$ per game.

The expected long-term gain for player 2 is given by:

$3 - 4 \times \frac{8}{11} = \frac{1}{11}$

i.e. Player 2 will gain on average $\frac{1}{11}$ per game.

DECISION AND DISCRETE MATHEMATICS — RECURRENCE RELATIONS

AQA: D2

First order linear recurrence relations

A recurrence relation is of the first order if the difference between the highest and the lowest subscripts is 1. It is of the form $x_n = ax_{n-1} + b$ where a and b are constants. The **general solution** to a first order recurrence relation of the form $x_n = ax_{n-1} + b$ is given by:

$x_n = a^n x_0 + b \left(\frac{a^n - 1}{a - 1}\right)$ where $a \neq 1$.

Example

Find the general solution of $x_n = 3x_{n-1} + 5$ given $x_0 = 2$.

Solution

$a = 3$, $b = 5$, $x_0 = 2$.

Substituting these into $x_n = a^n x_0 + b \left(\frac{a^n - 1}{a - 1}\right)$ gives:

$x_n = 3^n \times 2 + 5 \left(\frac{3^n - 1}{2}\right)$

$\quad = 3^n \left(2 + \frac{5}{2}\right) - \frac{5}{2}$

$\quad = \frac{9}{2} \times 3^n - \frac{5}{2}$

Second order linear recurrence relations

A recurrence relation is of the second order if the difference between the highest and lowest subscripts is 2. There are two types of relations which you need to know.

- **Homogeneous linear recurrence relations**

    A second order linear recurrence relation is homogeneous if all its terms include xs to the power 1. It is of the form:
    $x_n = ax_{n-1} + bx_{n-2}$ where $n \geq 2$

    Dividing by x_{n-2} leads to the **auxiliary equation**, which is a quadratic of the form:
    $x^2 - ax - b = 0$
    The general solution will depend on whether the auxiliary equation has **two distinct roots** or **equal roots**.

- For two distinct roots y and z, the general solution is:
  $x_n = Ay^n + Bz^n$
- For equal roots k, the general solution is: $x_n = Ak^n + Bnk^n$
- **Non-homogeneous linear recurrence relations**

  A second order linear recurrence relation is non-homogeneous if it is of the form:

  $x_n = ax_{n-1} + bx_{n-2} + p$

  where $n \geqslant 2$ and p takes the form $cn + d$ or k^n.

  The general solution will be of the form:

  $x_n = $ (homogeneous solution) + (particular solution)

  In the exam, you will be given the form of the particular solution.

Example

Find the general solution of $x_n - x_{n-1} - 12x_{n-2} = 60n - 17$, given that a particular solution is of the form $cn + d$.

Solution

The auxiliary equation is $x^2 - x - 12 = 0$, i.e.

$(x - 4)(x + 3) = 0 \Rightarrow x = 4$ or $^-3$.

The homogeneous solution of
$x_n - x_{n-1} - 12x_{n-2} = 0$ is $x_n = A4^n + B(^-3)^n$.

Substituting $x_n = cn + d$ in the original recurrence relation gives:

$cn + d - [c(n - 1) + d] - 12[c(n - 2) + d] = 60n - 17$
$cn + d - cn + c - d - 12cn + 24c - 12d = 60n - 17$
$\qquad\qquad\qquad -12cn + 25c - 12d = 60n - 17$

i.e. $^-12c = 60 \Rightarrow c = ^-5$ and $25c - 12d = ^-17 \Rightarrow d = ^-9$

$\therefore$ A particular solution is $x_n = ^-5n - 9$

The general solution of the recurrence relation is in the form:

$x_n = A4^n + B(-3)^n - 5n - 9$

DECISION AND DISCRETE MATHEMATICS — CODING

AQA: D2

Binary codes

A binary code is a code of which the elements can assume one of two possible states. The message to be transmitted will consist of 1s and 0s. The set {1, 0} is called the **alphabet** for these codes. The word block indicates that the code will consist of **codewords** – containing 1s and 0s – of constant length n.

Detecting errors

One method for detecting errors arising when coded messages are sent, known as a **parity check**, involves adding an extra digit at the end of each codeword. This keeps the number of 1s even (even parity) or odd (odd parity) by placing an extra 1 or 0 at the end of the codeword. The sender calculates the parity and attaches a parity bit to the data. The receiver checks that the parity is consistent with the received message. If it is not, then an error must have occurred.

This method has limited usefulness as it can only detect an odd number of errors. However, if errors are relatively few this should not be a problem in practice.

Hamming code

Simple parity can detect single bit errors but does not allow them to be corrected, since you must identify the position of the incorrect bit, to correct it. The **hamming code** is an error control method allowing correction of single bit errors. For this, you must calculate the **hamming distance** – a measure of the difference between two codewords, expressed by the number of bits that must be changed to obtain one from the other. 0101 and 1001 have a hamming distance of 2. The concept of hamming distance is important in error detection. If a codeword containing an error is received, the codeword **nearest** to it, from the list of codewords defining the code, is the corrected code. The nearest codeword is the one from the list that produces the shortest distance from the received message.

For a hamming code to be able to handle up to k errors, the minimum hamming distance needs to be at least $2k + 1$.

DECISION AND DISCRETE MATHEMATICS — CODING

Example

The 16 valid codewords with a minimum hamming distance of 3 are the legal codewords in this system.

0000000	0000111	0011001	0011110
0101010	0101101	0110011	0110100
1001011	1001100	1010010	1010101
1100001	1100110	1111000	1111111

Suppose the string 0 1 1 1 0 1 1 is received. Which of 16 legal codewords do you think the string is most likely to represent?

Solution

The intended string is the one with the shortest hamming distance from the string 0 1 1 1 0 1 1.

The hamming distance for each legal codeword is as follows.

5	4	2	3
2	3	1	4
3	5	3	4
4	5	3	2

∴ the string is most likely to be 0 1 1 0 0 1 1 as that has the shortest hamming distance.

Linear codes

Any two codewords can be added using the rules:

$1 + 0 = 0 + 1 = 1$, $0 + 0 = 0$ and $1 + 1 = 0$.

If the sum of any two codewords from a code simplify to a codeword which belongs to the code then the code is said to be **linear**.

Note: Each linear code must contain a codeword containing only zeros as any codeword added to itself results in a codeword made entirely of zeros.

Index

acceleration 36, 38, 55, 63
acceptance region 74
alternative hypothesis 74, 83, 85
amplitude 62, 64
angles between two lines 20, 28
angular SHM 64
angular speed 54
approximate changes 4
asymptotes 7, 15
auxilliary equation 89

banked tracks 57
binary codes 91
binomial distribution 68, 77
binomial expansion 6
bits 91

Cartesian form 14, 31
central limit theorem 71
centre of mass 49–53
centripetal force 57
chain rule 1
circle 14, 16, 54, 55, 56
codeword 91, 92
coefficient of restitution 44, 45
composite bodies 51
confidence intervals 73, 80, 81
confidence limits 80
conical pendulum 55
conservation of momentum 43, 44, 45
contingency tables 85
continuity correction 68, 69, 72, 77, 79, 85
convenience sampling 70
correlation coefficient 82, 83

critical region 74
critical values for z-tests 75
cumulative distribution function 66
curves 14–16

differentiation 1–3, 17, 18, 37
direction vector 28, 29, 30
displacement 33, 34, 35, 36
distance 37, 37, 47, 56, 60, 63, 91
double angle identities 11
dynamics 36, 38

elastic potential energy 60
ellipse 15
energy 40, 41, 59, 61
equilibrium 47, 48
error correction 91
error detection 91
even powers of $\sin x$ and $\cos x$ 10
expectation 67
expectation algebra 67
exponential decay 22
exponential growth and decay 22–23
extension 60

first-order linear recurrence relations 89
force 33, 36, 38, 40–42, 44, 47, 48, 55–60
force time graph 44

goodness-of-fit tests 83–84
gravitational potential energy 40

hamming distance 91–92
homogeneous linear recurrence relations 89
Hooke's Law 60
hyperbola 15

identities 10
implicit functions 17
improper fractions 9
impulse 44
integrals - logarithmic function 11
integration 10, 12, 18–19, 32, 37, 52, 74
integration by parts 13
inverse functions differentiation 3

kinematics 36
kinetic energy 40, 59, 61

lamina 50–51
leaning ladders 48
linear codes 92
linear SHM 62–63
logarithmic functions 2, 11–12

mean 65, 68–73, 75–77, 80
mechanical energy 40
median 49, 66
mid-ordinate rule 32
mixed strategy 86
modulus of elasticity 60
moments 47, 48
momentum 43, 45

Newton's Law of Cooling 22
Newton's experimental law 44, 45
Newton-Raphson method 32

Index

non-homogeneous linear recurrence relations 90
normal approximation 68, 77–79
normal distribution 67, 68, 69, 72, 77, 79
null hypothesis 74, 76–78, 82, 85
numerical integration 32

oblique impact 46
odd powers of $\sin x$ and $\cos x$ 11

pairs of lines 29–30
parabola 15
parametric differentiation 14–15
parametric form 14–15
parallel vector 28, 37, 38
parametric integration 20
parity check 91
partial fractions 8–9, 12
pay-off matrix 86, 87
perpendicular vector 28
planes 31
play-safe strategies 86, 87
points of inflexion 5, 7
Poisson approximation 68
Poisson distribution 65, 68, 69
Poisson mean 79
population parameter 70
potential energy 40, 59, 60
power 42, 75
probability density function 66

probability 66, 68, 69, 72, 75, 75, 77, 78, 80, 86, 83
product moment correlation coefficient 82
product rule 1, 2
projectiles 33–35
proportions 72–73
pure strategy 86

quadratic factors 8
quota sampling 70
quotient rule 1

radial acceleration 54
random sampling 70
random variables 66–67
rational functions 7, 8
rectangular distribution 67
recurrence relations 89–90
rejection region 74, 76, 83

saddle point 86
sample size 71, 77, 78, 79–80, 81
sampling distribution 71–72
sampling techniques 70
scalar products 28
scalars 36
second-order linear recurrence relations 89–90
separation of variables 38–39
series 6
significance level 74–75, 77
significance test 74
simple pendulum 64

Simpson's rule 32
small angle approximations 5
Spearman's rank correlation coefficient 82
speed 36–37
springs 60–61
stable solution 86–87
standard deviation 71, 72, 75, 76, 79
standard error 71, 72
stratified sampling 70
systematic sampling 70

t-distribution 79–82
test statistic 74
test value 74
trapezium rule 32
trajectory formula 35
trigonometric functions 2–3, 5, 10–11
Type I error 75
Type II error 75

unbiased estimate 70–71
uniform lamina 50–51, 52
uniform solid 52

variance 66, 67, 68, 69, 71, 81
vector equations 28, 29
vectors 24–31, 54, 76, 77
velocity 33–34, 36–37, 46, 54
vertical circle 59

work 40–41, 60

zero-sum game 86–88
z-tests 75–76